Knowledge Set

Safeguarding Vulnerable Adults

Caroline Morris

Heinemann is an imprint of Pearson Education Limited, a company incorporated in England and Wales, having its registered office at Edinburgh Gate, Harlow, Essex, CM20 2JE. Registered company number: 872828

www.heinemann.co.uk

Heinemann is the registered trademark of Pearson Education Limited

First published 2008

12 11 10 09 08
10 9 8 7 6 5 4 3 2 1

British Library Cataloguing in Publication Data is available from the British Library on request.

ISBN 978 0 435402 37 2

Edited by Jane Anson
Typeset by Saxon Graphics Limited, Derby
Original illustrations © Pearson Education Limited 2008
Cover photo © FlowerPhotos.com/Noelle Pollington
Printed in the UK by Ashford Colour Press Ltd

Photo acknowledgements
Every effort has been made to contact copyright holders of material reproduced in this book. Any omissions will be rectified in subsequent printings if notice is given to the publishers.The author and publisher would like to thank the following individuals and organisations for permission to reproduce photographs:
Pages 4, 7, 17, 20, 35 © Pearson Education Ltd/Lord and Leverett; pages 5, 13, 24, 28, 78, 87, 92, 97 © Pearson Education Ltd/Jules Selmes; page 31 © Pearson Education Ltd/Richard Smith; pages 37, 67 © Pearson Education Ltd/MindStudio; page 40 © Corbis Premium RF/Alamy; page 45 © Bubbles Photolibrary/Alamy; page 48 © Janine Wiedel Photolibrary/Alamy; page 50 © Nordicphotos/Alamy; page 63 © Vstock/Alamy; page 73, 83 © Pearson Education Ltd/Gareth Boden.

Websites
The websites and weblinks used in this book were correct and up to date at the time of publication. It is essential for tutors to preview each website before using it to ensure that the URL is still accurate, relevant and appropriate.

Contents

Introduction

Knowledge sets have been created by Skills for Care, part of the sector skills council. The idea behind each knowledge set is to provide key learning outcomes for specific areas of work within adult social care. This means that employers and training providers can use a knowledge set to provide in-house training as part of employees' continuing professional development. The advantage of using a knowledge set for the basis of training is that both employers and those who have undertaken training can be assured that a minimum standard has been reached. The knowledge sets also ensure consistency in knowledge and understanding across organisations and services.

The knowledge set for Safeguarding Vulnerable Adults is aimed at those working in health and social care, supporting vulnerable adults. This book has been written by Caroline Morris, who has worked in the health and social care sector for over 20 years, in roles varying from nursing, training and development to care management.

Using this book, in conjunction with the Skills for Care knowledge set, will:

- provide essential learning for all aspects of safeguarding and protection, improving confidence and skills
- improve practice in order to meet the individual needs of those who receive care, allowing the opportunity to make a real difference
- support those completing NVQ and other training, providing evidence for portfolios
- support transition between different service settings in the health and social care sector
- ensure up-to-date and good practice.

The book is divided into the four main areas of the knowledge set:

- Roles and boundaries
- Danger, harm and abuse
- Social norms, values and perceptions
- Legislation and guidance in relation to the safeguarding of vulnerable adults.

These sections are further broken down into manageable topics, with spreads covering one or more learning outcomes. The following features have been designed to enhance the learning experience:

Activities – completion of the suggested activities and tasks will develop understanding and skills.

Care scenarios – real-life situations allowing knowledge to be put into practice.

Look it up – pointers to recognised reference sources that allow comparison of current knowledge with accepted good practice. You may also be asked to investigate your care setting's current procedures and practices.

Reflection – explore your level of knowledge as well as your thoughts, actions and behaviours.

Remember – key concepts and facts are highlighted and reinforced.

Question check – test your understanding and recall of a topic.

Space has often been provided for note-taking or the completion of activities and tables, although a notebook or work book can be used alongside this book in order to expand on certain areas.

This book not only covers the learning outcomes for those undertaking training, but also includes a section for those developing or leading training sessions. The Trainer notes provide the answers to Care scenarios, guidance on the completion of activities and also expands on the knowledge given in the four main knowledge set areas. In addition, guidance on activities within the book often includes ideas and suggestions for developing an activity and expanding on learning opportunities. Useful icons appear with each activity guidance feature, suggesting how long to spend on the activity and any materials that will be needed (e.g. pens, flipchart, OHP).

The Student log section of this book details all four main areas of the knowledge set for Safeguarding Vulnerable Adults, along with the learning outcomes. Space is provided for trainees to log their progress and record those learning outcomes they have covered. In addition, the tables can also be used to map the content of this book against NVQs and any other relevant training being undertaken.

For many people, starting work in the health and social care sector means coming to terms with the fact that some individuals will be subjected to abuse by those who are supposed to care for them.

Whatever your previous experience, coming face to face with situations involving abuse is not easy and can be emotionally demanding. Knowing what you are looking for and how to recognise it is vital. Taking the right steps when faced with abuse is the second part of your key contribution to individuals you provide care for.

Used either as part of the training package or on its own by an individual, this *Knowledge Set: Safeguarding Vulnerable Adults* will prove to be an invaluable resource for those developing their career in the adult health and social care sector.

Acknowledgements

The publisher would like to thank Skills for Care for giving permission to reproduce the tables of learning outcomes used in the Student log section of this book (see pages 112–18). Thanks also to Nigel Walker at Cornwall County Council.

The author would like to thank all those professionals who have given their advice and expertise for this book, and Pen Gresford for her guidance and encouragement throughout. She would also like to thank all her family and friends, for their tolerance and support.

1 Roles and boundaries

1.1 Understand the role, responsibilities and boundaries of the worker with regard to safeguarding individuals from danger, harm and abuse

'Adult abuse is unacceptable and all adults have the right to live their life free from abuse.' (Nigel Walker, Cornwall County Council's Executive Member for Adults)

It is clear that abuse of vulnerable people happens in different settings and among all sectors, but the range and extent are difficult to assess. In writing this book it would have been useful, for example, to have had access to more information on abuse within the learning disability sector or among young adults, but this was difficult to obtain. At the start of an elder abuse awareness campaign in 2006, Tracey Roose of Age Concern Cornwall said: 'Older people are at risk of, and suffer from, all kinds of abuse: emotional, physical, sexual and financial. Raising awareness of the potential for abuse to happen is the first vital step in stopping abuse from happening.'

There has been limited research into the nature and extent of elder abuse, and it is often suggested that the absence of data is a reflection of the low priority given to this area of the sector. Evidence from the Action on Elder Abuse (AEA) helpline in the UK identifies women as victims in 67% of calls. Domestic violence or psychological abuse in later life may have been going on for some time, or may begin with retirement or the onset of ill-health. It has been established that abuse increases with age, with 78% of victims being over 70 years of age. According to the AEA helpline in the UK, abuse happens mainly in the family home (64%), followed by residential care (23%) and then hospitals (5%). But it must be remembered that a helpline does not necessarily provide a true reflection of these incidents and many may go unrecorded. (http://www.elderabuse.org.uk)

In this section you will learn about the role of support services in protecting individuals from danger, harm and abuse.

What you need to learn

- Person-centred approach.
- Care planning.
- Risk assessment.
- The setting.

Person-centred approach

Feeling safe is an important part of well-being. Everyone has the right to protection from harm and abuse, and as a care worker you have an important role in monitoring and reporting any signs of abuse, neglect or other harm. However, it is important to carry out your role in a way that supports the roles and responsibilities of others. Knowing what to do and who to report to is an important part of safeguarding and protecting individuals.

Care scenario: Giselle

Giselle lives in a residential care home. She is 72 years old and very mobile, but has mild symptoms of dementia. Giselle insists on sitting in the same chair every day, but there is one member of staff who will not let her do this. This causes Giselle to become confused and agitated.

1. Is there abuse or harm happening in this situation? Explain what you think is going on.
2. What could staff do to help make the situation better and prevent it from happening again?

If Giselle wishes to sit in the same chair every day, she should be supported to do so, as the routine will reduce her anxiety and confusion and make her more relaxed in her surroundings. Preventing her from sitting where she wants to is a form of psychological abuse, causing potential and actual distress to Giselle.

The member of staff who has been preventing Giselle from sitting in her preferred place must be informed why this causes Giselle to become anxious. They should be supervised and monitored to ensure they do not continue to do this.

As a potential care worker it is part of your role to protect individuals from:

- **neglect** or **acts of omission**
- physical, sexual, emotional harm
- abuse.

It is part of your role as a care worker to protect individuals from neglect, physical, sexual, emotional harm and abuse. It is important that you do this while respecting the **diversity**, difference, preferences and choices of individuals with whom you work. The people you come into contact with may include individuals receiving services, volunteers, visitors, their friends and family, as well as peers and professional colleagues.

neglect/acts of omission

failure to provide care, food, warmth, clothes or treatment

diversity

individual characteristics or differences based on, for example, religion, culture, sexuality, gender or disability

Carer at work

Your responsibility to protect others includes identifying and monitoring of risks, including any potential **danger**, damage and destruction to the environment and goods, injury and harm to people, self-harm, bullying, abuse and reckless behaviour. This responsibility also includes the collecting and handling of information in an objective and non-judgemental way to ensure that any evidence that might be used in an abuse investigation is not prejudicial, or adversely affected.

According to the National Minimum Standards for Care Homes for Older People, abuse is defined as *a single or a repeated act, omission or lack of appropriate action, occurring within a relationship of care or trust, which causes distress, harm or injury.*

This definition allows several different types of abuse to be recognised, including neglect, **physical abuse**, **psychological abuse**, **sexual abuse**, racial or cultural abuse and **financial abuse**.

danger
being at risk from harm or injury

physical abuse
inflicting pain or injury on an individual

psychological abuse
upsetting or humiliating an individual using words or actions

sexual abuse
any sexual act that is carried out without permission

financial/material abuse
the illegal use or misuse of property or items without permission from the person they belong to

Think about your roles and what might be asked of you in relation to the protection of individuals. What would your role be? Who could support you to carry this out?

Activity 1

Ask where you can find copies of your workplace's policies relating to the support available to staff carrying out your job role.

Individuals should be encouraged to participate in their care planning

Are you involved in writing or reviewing care plans? How much is the individual involved in making decisions about their care?

person-centred approach
assessing an individual's needs, putting them at the centre of the process

rights
legal or moral entitlement to choice, freedom, privacy and services

The rights of the individual

The **rights** of individuals are protected by the Commission for Social Care Inspection (CSCI). In their publication *Care Homes for Older People*, CSCI indicate that individuals have the right to:

- privacy and dignity
- choice and control
- express their cultural and spiritual needs
- health and well-being
- socialise and participate in social activities
- good food
- a clean, comfortable and safe home
- protection from harm and abuse.

The rights of individuals are also protected by legislation (laws), which can be a long and complicated process. If required, people and organisations have to be properly consulted on the idea; the Bill has to be written in a way that will be accepted by Parliament and then it is thoroughly debated. A Bill has to pass through many stages in Parliament before it can be given what is known as Royal

Select one of the statements from the CSCI's *Care Homes for Older People* and consider how you carry this out in your job role. Does this meet the needs of the individuals you provide care for?

Protection of Vulnerable Adults (POVA)

a scheme launched by the Department of Health in 2004. At the heart of the POVA scheme is the POVA list of care workers who have harmed vulnerable adults in their care. From 26 July 2004, registered care providers must request a check against the POVA list when considering a person for a care position

self-esteem

an individual's confidence in themselves

care planning

a way of agreeing, arranging and managing the services or help needed to support someone to live at home, receive treatment or live in a more supported environment

Assent and become law. Bills can be introduced into either the House of Commons or the House of Lords.

For example, the Human Rights Act (1998) includes an individual's right to:

- freedom from torture and inhuman or degrading treatment
- liberty and security of person
- respect for private and family life, home and correspondence
- freedom of thought, conscience and religion
- freedom of expression
- freedom of assembly and association
- peaceful enjoyment of possessions and protection of property.

The Human Rights Act, Article 9: Freedom of thought, conscience and religion, guarantees that you can think what you want and can hold any religious belief. You cannot be forced to follow a particular religion and cannot be stopped from changing your religion.

The Care Standards Act 2000 includes provision for a Protection of Vulnerable Adults (POVA) register to be kept of all those people considered unsuitable to work with vulnerable adults. Care organisations can contribute to this register by reporting any proven cases of abuse, and by referring to the register whenever recruiting new staff.

In order to maintain an individual's **self-esteem**, it is important that you take a positive approach towards their care. You can do this by:

- encouraging them to be independent and to make their own decisions
- respecting them as individuals and not behaving in a discriminatory way
- ensuring that you respect the confidentiality of any information they give you
- encouraging them to participate in their **care planning**.

Personal preferences and cultural, social and religious needs

The **person-centred approach** to planning is about how we put the individual's needs first. The best way you can do this is by finding out what is important to individuals in order to support them towards taking control of their lives and living in the way they choose. Through the person-centred approach you can help individuals to think about what they want from their lives, and express their dreams and wishes. Using this approach helps individuals decide what is important to them and choose how they are supported to achieve what they want to. Through person-centred planning, you are able to identify how best to support people and how friends and family and other social networks can help with this support.

Person-centred care aims to see the person as an individual, rather than looking just at their illness or condition and the abilities they may have lost. Instead of treating the person as a collection of symptoms and behaviours that need to be controlled, the person-centred approach takes into account their unique qualities, abilities, interests, preferences and needs.

Person-centred care means seeing each person as an individual

Care scenario: Sarah

Sarah is 39 years old. She was diagnosed at the age of 21 with schizophrenia. Sarah was staying up all night to do washing and cleaning, and constantly walking about her local area, talking and singing. She never showed any violent tendencies to other people or to herself, but her parents were elderly and could not cope with her. Sarah is intelligent and lively, but because of her constant activity she was unable to keep a job for any length of time. Her condition is controlled with medication.

1. How can Sarah be supported to plan for her care?
2. What care needs will Sarah have?

When you are working with individuals it is important to consider all aspects of their needs and preferences.

- Cultural preferences or needs include the beliefs and customs that individuals have grown up with and learnt from family, carers and friends. Cultural needs include observing prayer times and religious holidays and wearing cultural or traditional clothing, headwear or jewellery.
- Social preferences or needs include who they like to mix with, what they have in common with others.
- Religious preferences or needs include what beliefs the individual has. They may have a preferred faith and time needs to be spent finding out how they wish to express this faith.

A care plan must be tailored to suit the individual's needs.

Activity 2

Complete the table to show how you would meet the needs of individuals in the identified areas. Also state what you think might happen if these needs are not properly met. An example is given to help you.

Personal preference or need	How this can be met	Consequences if this need was not met
To maintain contact with friends from church	Ensure that this is a priority when planning; arrange regular visits to and from friends	The individual could feel isolated and might become withdrawn
To practise their faith as they wish		
To follow a preferred diet		
To observe Ramadan		
To watch their favourite football team play every match		
To go to the theatre when they want to		

Care planning

The purpose of planning

The most important person in the care-planning process is the individual receiving the service, so they must be clear about how to provide initial information about their choices and how to feedback on the way the care package is working. On-going monitoring and review can make sure that needs are being met and that changes are made when necessary.

Once you understand people's needs and wishes, you can bring together all the people who are important to an individual, to define the best way for support to be offered. This may include:

- friends
- family
- carers
- GP/nurse
- **multi-disciplinary team**
- other agencies involved in the provision of support or care.

multi-disciplinary team
team whose members work together to deliver services

Care planning is not about providing the support of the service, it's about asking what is possible when offering care, advice or support and when building community and other relationships. If an individual's needs are not properly met, the individual may feel that they are not able to make any choices, or that they are not cared for. As a result, their health may suffer or their dependence on the service may increase.

The stages of planning

Care planning involves a systematic assessment and recording of individual needs within the service user's care plan. It follows the cycle shown below:

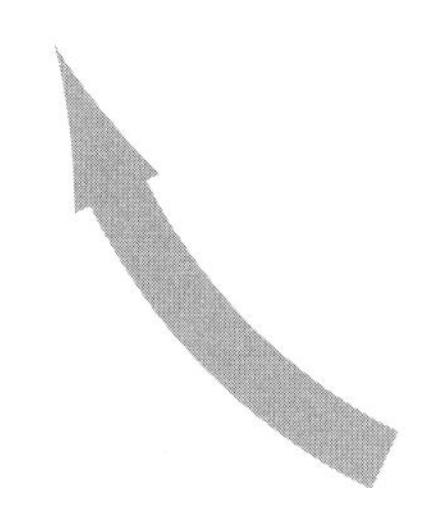

The care-planning cycle

A care plan must be reviewed on a regular basis.

Therefore, the care plan should contain the following information:

1. An individual's particular care needs or problems.
2. The main reasons for providing care.
3. The goals that the care activities are designed to achieve.
4. The care activities that are being provided in order to achieve the goals.
5. The agreed timescales for achieving the goals, including a review date.
6. How the care plan is to be reviewed and updated to ensure the goals have been achieved.

Although it is important to maintain individuals' dignity and independence, there may be occasions when their personal preference conflicts with the total care that is required, or there may be a risk of injury to the individual or others. In these cases, the risk of maintaining individuals' personal preferences might outweigh the benefits. For example, while individuals who smoke might be able to smoke in their own room during the day, it is important that they understand that smoking unsupervised at night, and in bed, is a significant hazard to themselves and to others within the care home. However, a decision as to whether the individual may smoke can only be taken after a full and complete assessment of risk has been undertaken.

The care plan

Individual plan of care: Sunnydale Residential Care Home				
Name: Frances Hammond				
Date of plan: 21/11/2007				
Need	**Outcome**	**How to achieve it**	**Who is responsible**	**Review date**
Mobility	Full mobility and independence regained	On-going physiotherapy and exercise	Care staff/ Manager to oversee	2 months
To meet with friends from former home	Increased self-esteem	Arrange meetings with friends, arrange transport	Activities officer	1 month
Date of review: 21/12/2007				
Care plan agreed by: CM & NE				
Link worker: NE				

Care Plan: Caring Hands Domiciliary Care Agency				
Name: James Crawford				
Date of plan: 20/10/2007				
Need	**Outcome**	**How to achieve it**	**Who is responsible**	**Review date**
Support to wash, dress and prepare food	Maintenance of independence	Support until broken arm heals and on-going exercise	Agency Manager/ JC	2 weeks
A healthy diet	Support with shopping	Delivery of shopping arranged	Care worker	2 weeks
Date of review: 02/11/2007				
Care plan agreed by: AM & JC				
Link worker: N/A				

Activity 3

Ask your supervisor if you can access the care plan of one of the individuals you work with.

Describe three sources of information that you can use to make the care-planning process completely based around the needs of the individual.

Risk assessment

We are all at risk from abuse in some way; it is how we manage the risk that is important. For example, Internet fraud is on the increase but if we take measures to prevent this from happening, such as using only secure sites, the risk is reduced.

A vulnerable individual may be at risk of harm or abuse for a number of reasons, including:

- their level of communication and understanding
- their disability
- where they live, for example if they are living at home with carers calling in, or in a residential setting
- their understanding of what abuse is
- an awareness of their own safety.

Risk assessments must be recorded and made available to all staff.

However, individuals are often not able to minimise the risk themselves, so it is important to identify those at risk and to assess and monitor those risks. When a risk assessment has been carried out it is important that all staff involved in the delivery of care are aware of the actions to be taken, in order to avoid confusion and to offer a consistent approach to care provision.

If an individual is considered to be at risk, discussions will be held so that agreement can be found on how to deal with this. These discussions will take into account the individual's views on what kind of support they want, but will also include the opinions of the care setting and other key people involved in the delivery of care to the individual. Once agreement has been reached, it is important to always carry out activities according to this agreement.

If the individual does not agree with how you carry out an activity or procedure, discuss this with them and remind them of what has been agreed and why. It is important to acknowledge their right to make choices about their own care and protection, but also to remind them of the responsibilities that go with this. If they still object, you should seek advice from your manager.

Care scenario: Mrs Mills

Mrs Mills is 85 and lives on her own in a large house in a very secluded area. Her husband died some years ago and since then she has been supported by her granddaughter, who visits regularly. Mrs Mills is getting increasingly forgetful and often forgets to lock her door at night. Her granddaughter wants to go on holiday and after discussions with Mrs Mills has arranged for Mrs Mills to go into a care home for this period.

1. Is Mrs Mills at risk?
2. If there are risks, what do you think they are?
3. How can Mrs Mills be helped to be safe?

Who or what do you think you need to risk-assess? Why might this be?

'No Secrets'
guidance on developing and implementing multi-agency policies and procedures to protect vulnerable adults from abuse

local authority
regional council or local government

inter-agency framework
organisations demonstrating how they intend to plan and work together towards shared goals

Look for 'No Secrets' on the Internet. Make a note of the key points.

'No Secrets'

'No Secrets' is a set of guidelines published by the government about adult protection (see pages 86–7, 100–1). The guidelines state that older people have the right to be treated with respect, and to be supported to live in their own home and community without concerns or fears about physical or emotional harm or abuse.

The guidance also gives local authorities the role of co-ordinating all procedures relevant to the protection of vulnerable adults. Every **local authority** needs to have a multi-agency management committee to develop and oversee policy and practice.

The guidance includes:

- how to identify who is at risk from harm or abuse
- the recruitment and on-going training of staff
- how to develop and implement an effective **inter-agency framework** so that all organisations involved are aware of the correct procedures to follow.

The setting

Settings include:

- residential
- domiciliary care
- day care.

Residential settings include care homes, respite settings and short-stay hostels. Often individuals move permanently into a residential care setting, being provided with the care they need by staff within the setting.

Domiciliary care provides services to individuals with reduced ability to care for themselves, assisting them to continue living in their own homes.

Day-care settings include respite care, resource centres and facilities providing specific services such as lunch or skills training. In this section you will learn about the support that settings offer individuals and why this is so important.

Visitors should be asked to sign in

Visitors to the setting

You and the individuals you work with need to feel safe and secure. All workplaces will have a policy on visitors to ensure this. However, as a general rule you should always check the identity of all visitors by asking for identity badges and for a works telephone number so that you can ring and check the identity of a tradesperson or visitor. You should also:

- check with your manager that the visitor has permission to visit
- check that the individual wants to see the visitor
- check that the visitor completes the visitors' book; also give them a visitor's badge
- get to know regular visitors to the setting and introduce them to other staff
- know how to raise the alarm if you discover an intruder
- explain to individuals in their own home that their safety comes first, so they must check who is visiting.

Think about who might visit a setting in any one day. For example there may be family, friends, volunteers, GPs, nurses, pharmacists and tradesmen.

Can you think of any others?

Activity 4

Write down the key points you would include in a visitors' policy for a work setting of your choice. Make sure you include all aspects, for example a signing-in book, how to check a visitor's identity and the procedure for raising the alarm if you have concerns.

Security of the setting

As a worker in the sector it will be necessary for you to keep yourself, individuals and others safe and secure within the setting and to minimise any risks that have been identified. For example, you are responsible for the health and safety of individuals and their family and friends; you are also responsible for colleagues and co-workers. You will be responsible for these individuals within the setting, in an individual's home, or out in the community, wherever they participate in any activities, for work or pleasure.

In your work setting, see if you can find any records that require updating once they have been made. What do they relate to and what do they ask to be done?

A worker's responsibility includes the monitoring of workplace practices such as care activities; health and care procedures; and the use of activity and support materials and specialist equipment. This may involve carrying out regular checks to make sure doors are locked, or that fire doors are working properly. It may also involve checking hoists to make sure they are fully charged and working properly. Often these checks are written and recorded in a maintenance file to check and prove that they have been carried out.

Activity 5 – In your workplace

Identify potential hazards relating to each of the following:

1. Disposal of clinical waste.
2. Use of disinfectants.
3. Taking an individual shopping.

Environmental safety of the setting

In the work setting, often known as the environment, it is important that there is a work practice of efficient and effective safety and security. For example a regular scheduled safety check should be carried out, not only to check for potential safety risks but also to promote the culture of safety to the staff so that they learn about safety hazards and report conditions as they arise.

This procedure can produce such findings as hazardous walkways or passageways, fire doors wedged open, barriers and safety risks in treatment rooms; sharps containers within easy reach or furniture with sharp corners. Sharps containers ensure the safe disposal of items such as needles and blades, and are required in all care settings where these items are used.

It is also important to monitor for ways in which you can help to lower the risk of infection, such as making sure that sinks are clean, that there are gel dispensers for hand-hygiene and always following the recommended hand-washing guidelines. This may be more of an opportunity for your manager, but you can contribute to this by asking for sufficient provision.

Activity 6

What other aspects of the environment do you need to check on a regular basis to make sure health, safety and security are maintained?

1.2 Understand the role and responsibilities of the worker with regard to recognising potential and actual danger, harm and abuse

In this section you will learn about how feeling safe is an important part of well-being. Everyone has the right to protection from harm and abuse, and you have an important role in monitoring and reporting any signs of abuse, neglect or other harm.

What you need to learn

- Observation.
- Monitoring.
- Reporting and recording information.
- Confidentiality and the sharing of information.

Care scenario: Stacey

Stacey is a support worker in a residential setting for adults with learning disabilities. Stacey enjoys her job but has become concerned for the welfare of the individuals and thinks that they may not be being given the choices they should be. Regular mealtimes have become routine, with the same bland food being served all the time, and bedtimes have to be the same at all times. Staff plan activities for the evenings, by selecting things they think residents would like to do.

1. What is wrong about this situation?
2. What should Stacey do in her role as support worker?
3. Who could help Stacey to change things?

Observation

observation
looking at the actions and well-being of an individual

Observation is an activity that you, as a care worker, will carry out on a regular, often unplanned basis. It will soon become part of your daily routine. Observation makes sure that you know if individuals are well, and if there are any changes to their behaviour or well-being. Observation contributes to quality care provision and links to the National Minimum Care Standards.

Since 2004 the Commission for Social Care Inspection (CSCI) has had the responsibility for inspecting all adult care services in England, in Scotland it is the Scottish Commission for the Regulation of Care, the Care Standards Inspectorate for Wales and in Northern Ireland the Northern Ireland Social Care Council is responsible. Some services, for example housing-related support, are not regulated. The aim of this support is to develop and sustain an individual to live independently in their accommodation. Some examples of housing-related support services include working with individuals to enable them to access their full benefit entitlement or advising them on home improvements. Other services provided include a home visit for a short period each week or a full-time live-in support worker for a long period.

Observation of individuals in your care will enable you to recognise any change in their behaviour

The Commissions use the National Minimum Standards to inspect the quality of care delivery. Each type of service has a different standard, for example there are standards for care homes for younger adults and for care homes for older people. The standards provide a detailed guide, outlining the minimum standard of care that can be expected.

The National Minimum Standards for Care Homes for Older People ask that a four-stage approach to the problem of abuse is followed:

1. Prevention – as far as is practical or possible, care homes need to prevent abuse from happening at all.
2. Identification – where abuse does occur, homes need to identify it quickly and make sure that it is reported.
3. Action – once abuse has been identified, homes need to take quick action to deal with incidents and ensure the safety of their residents.
4. Planning – homes need to use learning from incidents of abuse in their planning for the future.

Observation is an important part of this process and contributes to the assessment and safe management of individuals who may be at risk from harm or abuse. In addition to being aware of the whereabouts and safety of the individual being observed, observation should involve making a continuous assessment of the level of risk. Observation is only one aspect of caring for individuals at risk. It should not just be a formal process but must be an activity that all staff are aware of and involved in. If an individual is thought to be at risk in any way then observations may be required to be recorded.

How is the individual behaving? Is there any change from what you know to be their usual behaviour? Changes may include loss of appetite, inability to sleep well, constantly chattering or seeking attention from you or other members of staff.

As a care worker, what is your role in watching how individuals behave, how well they seem to be or identifying any changes?

It is also important to monitor how staff are behaving. Staff can also be at risk from abuse, from the individuals they care for, from other staff or from the organisation they work for. Any concerns must be reported and recorded in an individual's care plan or diary, as appropriate. An incident report may have to be completed, but your senior or manager will advise you on this as appropriate.

Monitoring

Monitoring individuals is also carried out to prevent incidents, but may be required on an on-going basis if abuse has already taken place, so that it can be prevented from happening again. Included in your role and responsibilities in relation to the protection of individuals is minimising the levels of abuse within health and care environments, reducing the effects of abusive behaviour and monitoring individuals who are at risk from abuse, both named individuals who have been designated at risk and others.

Individuals at risk from abuse may be abusing themselves, such as through the use of substances or self-harming behaviours, or they may be at risk from abuse by another. If monitoring is to be carried out, a clear procedure needs to be followed and each setting will have guidelines on how to do this. Following procedures will make sure that monitoring does not interfere with other activities and that reports are accurate and make sense to the reader.

How will monitoring help to protect individuals at risk from harm or abuse?

Monitoring may be specifically requested for a particular reason, for example an indicidual may be particularly vulnerable due to illness or disability. Or they may be new to your setting and you need to monitor them to make sure they are settling in well.

Disclosure can have a huge impact on an individual. Monitoring and observation can take this into account and ensure that the individual feels safe and unthreatened.

Reporting and recording information

If you have suspicions about an incident or an individual has disclosed information to you, it is important to make a detailed note of what you have seen or what they have said, using your setting's incident record form if possible. Make sure this record is dated and signed and, if the incident or disclosure is witnessed by a colleague, that they also sign the report. This is also known as whistle-blowing (see pages 95, 100–101).

If you have serious concerns about the immediate safety of an individual, contact the Police or Social Services. Record the name of the person you spoke to and tell your manager what you have done.

Care plans, needs assessments, case reviews and day files are required as legal records of care and the keeping of certain confidential notes and records relating to individuals is an essential part of the communication and day-to-day running of a care home.

It is important that records are:

- factual, consistent and accurate
- written as soon as possible after an event has occurred
- written clearly, legibly and in pen, not pencil
- written so that any alterations or additions are dated, timed and signed in such a way that the original entry can still be read clearly
- clear, unambiguous and concise.

Records should not include:

- unnecessary abbreviations or jargon
- meaningless phrases, irrelevant speculation or offensive subjective statements
- irrelevant personal opinions regarding an individual or an incident.

Incident report

On 22 November 2007 one of my link workers, MM, approached me. A young person, CC, had disclosed actual abuse to him.

During the conversation MM wondered if other actions could have been taken to prevent the incident. MM was aware that with hindsight it was easy to identify signs and indicators of abuse, but when faced with contradictory and insubstantial evidence it is difficult to predict events. The social worker and health visitor had been in regular contact with CC, but much of the abuse was such that it left no mark. They had all felt that 'something was wrong' but were unable to explain exactly what it was. In the same way MM had felt that there was something wrong in this and other situations, but was not able to produce sufficient evidence to back up these feelings.

He spoke of the need to balance risks with safety and how this was difficult with young people. He identified a situation in the past where CC had been given a certain amount of freedom, but had run away. They had worked hard to earn this freedom and MM did not want to see this removed, but could see that this incident might mean that it would be.

However, CC had appeared very agitated during the afternoon and later asked to speak to MM about something. MM said he had told CC that what they said would be confidential

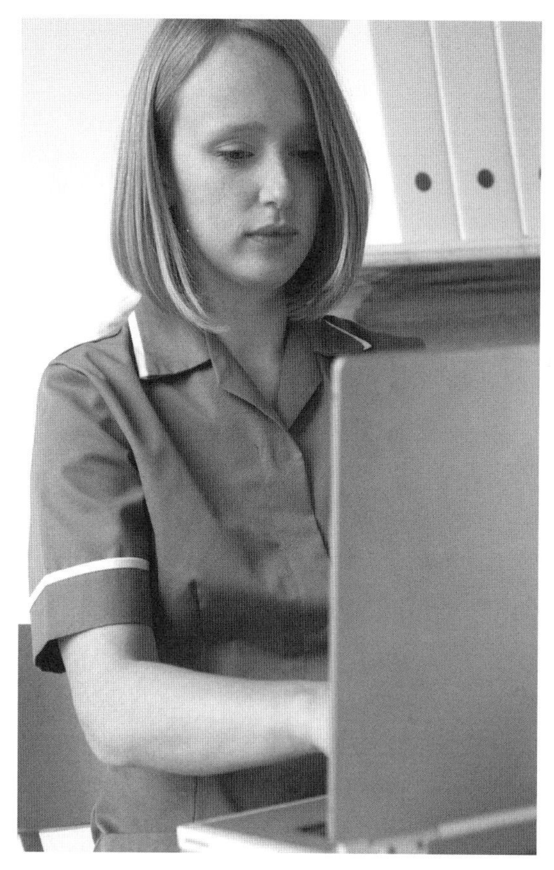

Carer completing records

unless CC was at risk or if others were at risk from harm or abuse. CC then broke down and said that abuse had been going on for some time but CC had been told not to tell anyone or they would come to harm. MM told CC that he would need to pass this information on so that MM's manager could do something to help. CC became distressed again at hearing this, so MM had to calm CC so they could carry on with the disclosure.

The rules governing the recording and use of information relating to individuals have been laid down by the Caldicott Report. The key requirements of this report are that all health and social care staff must:

1. Have a specific purpose for recording and using information relating to individuals.
2. Only record and use information when it is necessary.
3. Use only the minimum information required.
4. Only give access or have access to information on a strict 'need to know' basis.
5. Be aware of their responsibilities concerning the recording and use of information.
6. Understand and comply with the relevant laws e.g. the Data Protection Act 1998.

Activity 7

Care report, 21st October

Mac was OK this morning I think and seemed quite chatty, he does go on a bit though. Mac complaned as I told him to dress himself. He did this with a little help but moned as usual that he hadn't been sleeping well. Me and Maria think this is because Mac stayed up 2 late with the television on and then can't relax and go to sleep, but you know what he is like and there is no point in telling him. I then made his lunch; I didn't ask him what he wanted as he takes too long to decide. He ate it OK and drank plenty of fluids. While I was there the nurse called in to change his cafeter. All care given as required.

1. What would you consider to be the good aspects of this report?
2. What do you think are the poorer aspects of this report?
3. What changes can be made to the report to make it better?
4. Rewrite the report, taking into account your answers to the questions above.

Confidentiality and the sharing of information

Although it is important to maintain the dignity and independence of all individuals, there may be times when the personal preference of individuals might conflict with the total care that is required. Or there may be a risk of injury to the individual or others. In these cases, the risks might outweigh the benefits of maintaining individuals' preferences.

Confidentiality must be adhered to during the care-planning process. Agreement early on in the process between individuals, other staff, their families and carers over the sharing of information can help to prevent problems from occurring later on. It is necessary for the individual to give consent for information about their care needs and treatment to be shared with family, friends or carers. However, a lack of consent does not prevent staff listening to carers' concerns and providing them with general guidance and assistance. There are exceptional circumstances when confidentiality may be broken. These relate to issues of public safety, including the protection of vulnerable people. When others are deemed to be at risk, staff have a duty to inform them, for example if an individual states that they are going to injure or harm another person.

Care scenario: Sally

When Sally was readmitted to hospital in an acute psychotic state she repeatedly said that she did not want her husband, Mike, to be involved in any discussions or decisions about her care. However at an initial meeting with a member of staff from the community mental health team when she was well, Sally had given her permission for information and decisions to be shared with Mike if she became unwell again. As a result of this meeting staff felt able to include Mike in all aspects of Sally's care, without fear of breaching her right to confidentiality.

It is important that issues around confidentiality don't prevent staff from listening to families and carers. Staff should always discuss fully with individuals the need for families and carers to be given information so that they can continue to support them. However, it is more likely that carers will want to provide staff with personal details about the individual to help with the care plan. This might include simple facts about dietary preferences and needs or allergies or concerns about potential risks or dangerous behaviour that requires further monitoring. It is important that staff take the time to ensure that carers and family members feel their contributions to the care plan are valued.

1.3 Understand the role and responsibilities and boundaries of others with regard to safeguarding individuals from danger, harm and abuse

In this section you will learn about the roles of other workers and individuals in keeping people safe from harm. What do they have to do and how do they carry this out? It is important that you are aware of these roles so that you can access the support and advice you need for yourself and others.

What you need to learn

- The individual.
- Family and friends.
- Other workers and their roles.

The individual

The relationship between carer and individual is based on mutual trust. This is recognised by the GSCC Code of Practice, which states that social care workers must:

> (2) ...strive to establish and maintain the trust and confidence of individuals and carers. This includes:
>
> 2.1. Being honest and trustworthy.
>
> 2.2. Communicating in an appropriate, open, accurate and straightforward way.
>
> 2.3. Respecting confidential information and clearly explaining agency policies about confidentiality to individuals and carers.
>
> 2.4. Being reliable and dependable.
>
> 2.5. Honouring work commitments, agreements and arrangements and, when it is not possible to do so, explaining why to individuals and carers.
>
> 2.6. Declaring issues that might create conflicts of interest and making sure that they do not influence your judgement or practice.
>
> 2.7. Adhering to policies and procedures about accepting gifts and money from individuals and carers.

It is vital that this relationship is built and maintained when working in partnership with individuals, since it offers choice and empowerment, and supports the implementation of policies and procedures in relation to protection.

Care scenario: Sue Sharma

Sue Sharma is a unit manager on a specialist rehabilitation unit. She leads a team of ten staff, made up of both trained and untrained nursing staff. She is currently concerned about the attitude of some members of staff towards two patients: Mr Goshh and Mr Ashley. Mr Goshh is 62 and has had a road accident. His acute injuries have been treated. However, he must now receive more specialist care. Mr Goshh is a practising Muslim.

Sue has noted that staff avoid chatting to Mr Goshh and she has even noticed some staff ridiculing or ignoring him when he asked for help to get to the prayer room. Sue also noted that many clients object to Mr Goshh having a different choice of meals from other patients.

Mr Ashley is also a patient on the unit. Like Mr Goshh, his acute injuries have been treated and he is now receiving specialist care.

Sue has noted that staff appear happy to chat with Mr Ashley but avoid physical contact with him whenever they can. This means that his medical dressings are not being changed as often as they should. Sue was upset when she overheard some patients discussing his injuries and illness, in particular his HIV status, as this condition is not obvious and Mr Ashley has asked staff to keep this information confidential.

In an attempt to resolve some of the issues, Sue rewrote the policies that relate to Equal Opportunities. She used the code of practice called the Nursing and Midwifery (NMC) Code of Professional Conduct and also used Equal Opportunities legislation as her main source. All staff were then given training to make sure they understood the new policies. The policies were also made available to staff, patients and their families.

As a result of the new policies, many daily procedures were put into place, for example, all patients now have the same wide choice when ordering meals. Each evening they are given the menu and choose their meals for the following day. Mr Goshh is given much more assistance to meet his cultural needs and Mr Ashley receives the care he requires.

Activity 8

Read the following statements and suggest what the key issues are with each one. Is this working to best practice and ensuring the needs of individuals are met?

1. A voluntary sector organisation makes the decision to direct a major part of its funding into the care of older people rather than children's services.
2. A local authority has a policy of providing only meat-based meals-on-wheels to older community-care users.
3. A local housing association has a policy of not providing home adaptations for people who live in mobile homes, instead requiring them to move into residential accommodation.

Some organisations are not good at knowing whether the individuals they work with are safe from harm. Also, because of staff shortages, they sometimes allow people to work with individuals without checking whether this is safe.

Individuals are more at risk when people are allowed to work with them without proper checks. For this reason, anyone who employs people to work with vulnerable individuals must check the background of all prospective employees. They must make sure that a job applicant has never harmed anyone before, and that they are 'fit', that is according to police checks, job references, qualifications and experience.

What else might put an individual at greater risk?

It is also important that individuals are made as aware as possible of any potential risks they may face. This is not always easy, for example, an individual may have limited communication skills so may be unable to tell staff what is happening, or who the perpetrator is. Or they may be isolated and not see a lot of people, so have no one to tell about what is happening.

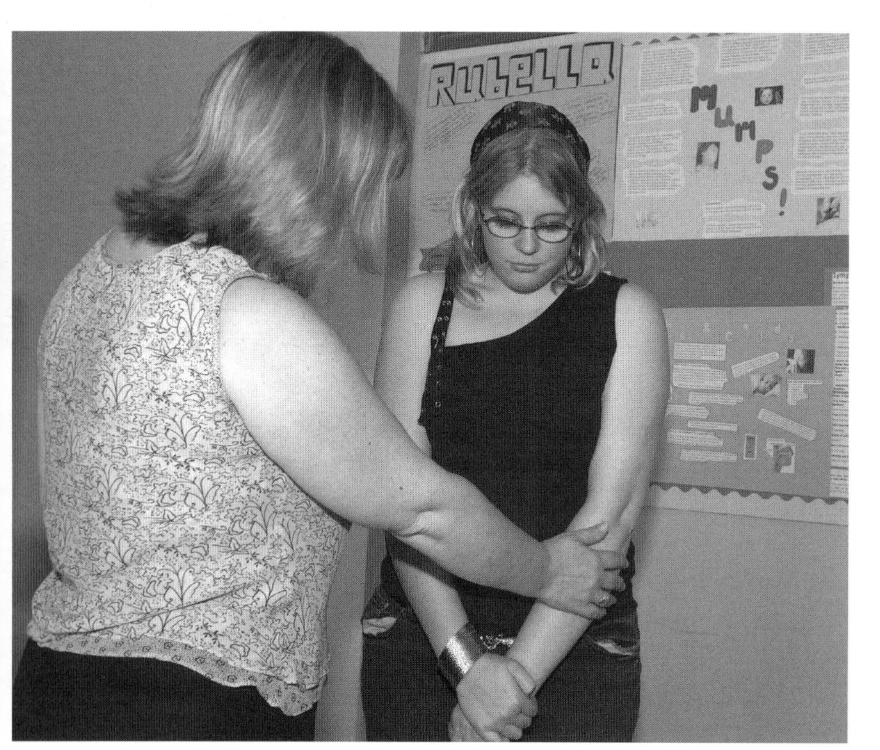

Dependence can make an individual vulnerable

Individuals must be encouraged to tell people if they are worried or anxious. Information on how to complain must be provided and when a complaint is made or information is disclosed this must be taken seriously.

Family and friends

Often family and friends are the main carers for an individual, so their role and responsibilities can be very complex. Informal carers, for example friends, neighbours or family, may not be aware of the policies and procedures they should be following or the signs and symptoms they should be looking out for. Informal carers may step in to provide care when there is a definite need, or perhaps when an individual cannot cope on their own; they are often unpaid. Friends may visit on an occasional basis and notice things that concern them, but not be aware of what to do. It is important that as much support and guidance is provided as possible. This may be done through formal or informal meetings or support groups.

Individuals who are dependent on others for their care needs are in a potentially vulnerable position, and may be at risk from those who might abuse the power and influence they have as a carer. It is the legal and moral responsibility of everyone working in a care setting to respect the rights of individuals and to protect them from physical or mental harm at all times.

The people who carry out abuse can be anyone who is in a position of trust with an individual and may include partners, children or other relatives, carers, friends or neighbours, volunteer workers, professional health-care staff or staff themselves. 'A position of trust' means anyone who works one to one with an individual or who has access to the individual, their home and finances. Care workers should notice when individuals are at risk of, or experiencing, neglect or abuse and respond appropriately to ensure that individuals are protected. Aspects that are known to contribute to harm or abuse include:

1. Prolonged **stress** amongst the care givers or care workers.
2. Feelings of resentment and hostility towards the individual.
3. Deeply held **prejudices** and **stereotypes** towards particular social groups, e.g. the elderly.
4. **Financial dependency** on the individual by a child or spouse.
5. Unrestricted access to an individual's finances by a child or spouse.
6. A limited ability or knowledge in caring for the individual.
7. Inadequate monitoring or supervision of a carer or care worker.

stress
emotional and physical strain caused by how we respond to different pressures

prejudice
judging someone or having an idea about them without actually knowing anything about them

stereotypes
generalisations or assumptions that people make about the characteristics of all members of a group, based on an (often wrong) image about what people in that group are like

financial dependency
relying on another person for money or resources

Activity 9

Mr Hughes lives alone. He is becoming increasingly forgetful and is showing the first signs of dementia. He eats very little and rarely goes out. Mr Hughes' son has responsibility for his finances but does not visit on a regular basis, so any care needed is carried out by friends or neighbours. Money for food and bills is not always available so neighbours or friends have to lend Mr Hughes money, which is not always paid back by the son.

1. What are the important issues here?
2. What can be done to make this situation better?

Other workers and their roles

Independent advocate

advocate
someone who can speak up to help another person's views be heard

advocacy
speaking up for another person to help them get their views across

Advocates aim to support people who need assistance to express their views and to have their stories heard, safeguarding people in situations where they are vulnerable. **Advocacy** is about standing up for and sticking with a person or a group, taking their side and helping them to get their point across. Advocacy adds weight to people's views, concerns, rights and aspirations. Independent advocacy reduces any possibility of conflict of interest, ensuring loyalty to the individual or group and no one else.

Advocacy is a part of everyday life, but sometimes when individuals are at a greater risk of poor treatment and when they most need to have someone to offer support, they do not have anyone who can help. Some people need advocacy on a long-term basis and other people only need it during a particularly difficult time. For example, someone may be able to speak up for themselves in everyday life, but may feel vulnerable and powerless when receiving treatment in hospital.

There are several approaches to advocacy that can offer support to individuals:

- Peer or Collective Advocacy – individuals come together to explore ways to get their voices and stories heard. This often results in a group voice being heard, which is generally stronger than a lone voice.
- Independent Professional Advocacy – the advocate, usually provided through an agency with this type of expertise, represents an individual's interests to help them to put their point more effectively. The advocate can be a paid or volunteer worker as part of a specific advocacy service.
- Citizen Advocacy – an unpaid citizen gets to know an individual in a vulnerable situation and promotes their interests over a longer period of time. A citizen advocate will initially receive support from an advocacy service, but this will be reduced as the partnership develops. Citizen advocacy can help to promote the independence of a very dependent person relying only on paid support.
- The Independent Mental Capacity Advocate (IMCA) Service is a type of statutory advocacy which was introduced by the Mental Capacity Act 2005. The Act gives people who lack capacity the right to receive support from an IMCA. In the main the individuals who will access the service are likely to be people with learning disabilities, older people with dementia, people who have an acquired brain injury or people with mental-health problems. IMCAs may also be accessed when people have a

temporary lack of capacity because they are unconscious or barely conscious, perhaps because of an accident or being under anaesthetic.

Many will have problems with communication and will be unable to liase with the advocate themselves. In addition, it is likely that many people using the service will be unable to express a view about the proposed decision.

An advocate will always try to get to know the individual's preferred method of communication and will spend time finding out if a person is able to express a view and how they communicate. IMCAs will be experienced at working with people who have difficulties with communication.

Has there been a time when you would have liked someone to speak up for you or to have been with you through a difficult period? How would this have helped you? Would you ask for advice or support in future?

Manager of service

A manager of a service must be registered, and their application will need to show that the service meets the following laws, regulations and standards:

- Care Standards Act 2000
- National Care Standards Commission (Registration) Regulations 2001

N.B. The National Care Standards Commission became the Commission for Social Care Inspection in April 2004, but the name of the regulations has not changed.

The manager of a service holds a very important and varied role. They are likely to be an experienced and competent worker with an in-depth knowledge of abuse and the importance of safeguarding individuals. Managers are responsible for the day-to-day running of homes. They oversee all activities within the home and make sure the quality of the service and care provided is maintained. Managers usually specialise in working with one specific client group such as:

- older people
- people with mental-health problems
- people with learning disabilities
- young adults
- the terminally ill
- people with physical disabilities
- children at risk
- families.

Activity 10

Think about the role of your manager of service: their knowledge and skills need to cover many areas.

Fill in the boxes below, suggesting the different roles and skills a manager may need, for example: good communication skills when working with staff and individuals.

Knowledge	Skills

Look on the CSCI website. What is its key function? What information would you find useful on its website? How many sets of standards are there on the site?

Managers need to ensure that the service meets a set of National Minimum Standards, which vary depending on the client group in the home. Standards are issued by the Department of Health and can be found on the Commission for Social Care Inspection website, www.csci.org.uk.

These standards include the requirement to ensure that the health, safety and welfare of individuals are promoted and protected, with other requirements relating to staff, safety and security, finances and the day-to-day running of the home.

Social worker

Almost all social workers start their careers with experience in social care, often branching out into a chosen part of the sector such as learning disabilities or mental health. Social workers form relationships with people and then as their adviser, advocate, counsellor or listener, they help individuals to live more successfully within their local communities by enabling them to find solutions to their problems. Social work involves engaging with individuals and their

Sorting out problems

families and friends, as well as working closely with other organisations including the Police, NHS, schools and probation service. Social workers are professionally qualified staff who assess the needs of individuals and plan the packages of care and support that will help them best. Becoming a social worker involves taking an honours degree in social work and registering with the relevant Care Council.

The roles that social workers undertake include working with individuals with mental-health problems or learning disabilities in residential care; working with offenders by supervising them in the community and supporting them to find work; assisting people with HIV/AIDS and working with older people at home, helping to sort out problems with their health, housing or benefits.

The role, as you can see, is based on supporting and protecting individuals, but also trying to promote independence as much as possible. Maintaining this balance is not always easy, as it can be difficult to promote independence while at the same time keeping risk to a minimum.

Care scenario: Mr Patel

Mr Patel lives alone, surviving on just a state pension. He has never claimed any other form of benefit, but does struggle to get by. He is becoming increasingly forgetful and is showing the first signs of dementia. He eats very little and rarely has the heating on – there is little money left over after paying bills. His carer has given him all the relevant information on benefits but he has not yet made a further claim. So Linda, his social worker, takes this forward on Mr Patel's behalf. Linda speaks to the benefits office and makes sure that Mr Patel is receiving all the benefits he should. As a result Mr Patel can now afford to have more help and can heat his house properly.

Activity 11

Look on the Internet or in a local or national daily newspaper – can you find any articles relating to the role of social workers?

1. What does the article say?
2. Is it positive or negative about the role?
3. Has this changed your views on social work as a profession?
4. Is there anything the social worker did that you consider to be wrong, or anything that appears to be good practice?

General practitioner

Because of their unique and continuing contact with individuals, GPs and other members of the multi-disciplinary team are well placed to recognise situations where individuals are at risk or are in need of protection, or where families or carers are in need of additional support. GPs, health visitors and practice nurses will have access to information about individuals and their families, and should be able to be part of the information-sharing process that is an essential part of the adult-protection process. The main forum for this is the adult-protection case conference. GPs should ensure that all members of their team know about local adult-protection procedures in keeping with their status and role in the protection of individuals from abuse or neglect. This should be supported by training in adult-protection.

GPs may also have on their lists 'looked-after children' who are in the care of local authorities, many of whom have unmet health needs and who may have been subjected to abuse or neglect.

Police

The main role of the Police in adult or child protection is to investigate criminal matters arising from cases of suspected or actual abuse. In the majority of cases of abuse, a criminal offence may have been committed. In such cases, the Police have a statutory duty to investigate the circumstances and to report the facts to social services and the relevant inspectorate. However, this duty is always balanced, with the welfare of the individual being paramount. Whenever there is a suspicion that a crime has been committed against an individual, or is still being committed, the Police should be informed immediately.

They will share information and consult as part of a multi-disciplinary assessment. They will attend Adult or Child Protection Case Conferences. Where they have reasonable cause to believe that an individual may be in need of compulsory supervision measures, they will pass information to social services, whether or not there are grounds for criminal prosecution.

Activity 12

Do you think the Police should be more or less involved in the identification of risk or harm and the protection of citizens? Why?

Fire service

The Fire Service is involved in safeguarding individuals through its role as an emergency service. Care settings are required to maintain their premises to the standards laid down by the Fire Service, verified through agreed fire checks and inspections. For example, they must appoint one or more **competent** people (depending on the size of the premises), to carry out duties associated with fire-risk prevention and assessment. A competent person is someone with enough training and experience or knowledge and other qualities to be able to implement these measures properly. Employers must also make sure that the premises and any equipment provided to be used for fire-fighting, detection and warning, or emergency routes and exits, are fully maintained by a person trained and competent to do this.

competent
properly or sufficiently qualified, capable or efficient

A key role of the Fire Service is to act in an advisory capacity, for example promoting the use of smoke alarms in homes.

After a fire, investigations may be carried out in order to establish the cause. The findings then contribute to risk-reduction to prevent other fires in similar situations.

The Fire and Rescue Act 2004 is the first major change in the law to impact on the operation of the service for more than 50 years. In 1947, when the previous Act was introduced, the Service was required to focus mainly on fire-fighting. Since then the role has evolved in a very different way and as a result the Fire and Rescue Authorities now also carry out the following roles:

- promoting fire safety
- preparing for fire-fighting
- dealing with emergencies such as flooding and terrorist attacks
- protecting people and property from fires.

Fire-fighting equipment must be checked regularly

In addition to these newly defined roles the service endeavours to put prevention in line with intervention and to use its resources as effectively and efficiently as possible to meet this role.

Specialist services

In addition to the statutory organisation there are many other services that provide advice and support to individuals, groups and organisations where there are adult- or child-protection concerns or allegations of abuse. Their roles can include advising government, a presence on Local Safeguarding Boards, liaising with the Police and Probation (MAPPA), and specialist agencies and other bodies on policy and practice and in individual cases. In addition, such organisations often run child-protection training courses throughout the UK, covering issues such as developing safe practice, appointing workers, dealing with allegations of abuse, and establishing adult- or child-protection policies.

Often, local specialist services are available in order to provide individuals with free, confidential advice and support, for example:

Victim Support – an independent charity that helps people cope with the effects of crime. They provide free and confidential support and information to help individuals deal with their experience. Victim Support can also provide a witness service to support individuals before, during and after a court appearance.

Carer's Information – this website contains articles, documents, links and other resources to support informal carers.

Women's Aid – a key national charity working to end domestic violence against women and children. Women's Aid supports a network of over 500 domestic and sexual violence services across the UK. Women's Aid also produces resources and information on a wide range of topics related to domestic violence.

Action on Elder Abuse – this organisation works to protect and prevent the abuse of vulnerable older adults. They were the first charity to confront these issues and are the only charity in the UK and Ireland working exclusively on the issue. Action on Elder Abuse runs a helpline which, although it cannot provide legal advice, can provide information on the nature of elder abuse and indicate what action might be taken in response to abuse or to prevent it.

VOICE UK – a national charity supporting people with learning disabilities and other vulnerable people who have experienced crime or abuse. VOICE UK also supports families, carers and professional workers, provides a telephone helpline and a range of training. It offers a range of training courses with an emphasis on a positive, practical approach to adult protection for participants working in health, police, social services, education, the criminal justice system and the voluntary sector. VOICE UK can also put individuals in touch with lawyers specialising in cases of abuse and crimes against people with learning disabilities.

The Princess Royal Trust for Carers – this is the largest provider of comprehensive carers' support services in the UK. It is made up of a network of 133 independently-managed Carers' Centres.

Activity 13

Using the Internet, media or journals, carry out some research into what support is available for individuals, their family and carers in the prevention of harm and abuse and in dealing with incidents. For example, what can Victim Support offer?

1. What is its key focus?
2. What service(s) does it provide?
3. Does it limit its provision to a particular group, such as children and young people?

The Social Care Inspectorate

The CSCI became operational on 1 April 2004 and combines the work previously carried out by the Social Services Inspectorate, Audit Commission Joint Review Team and the National Care Standards Commission. The main function of CSCI is to promote improvements in social care – across adult and children's services, in local councils, and in the voluntary and private sectors of social care.

Part of the function of CSCI is to assess the performance of local councils – including the work of the Adult Protection Committee – so as a result the Commission has changed its membership status on the committee from that of a full member to observer. Therefore CSCI has continued to take a full part in the committee discussions but has no voting rights.

Through its regulatory function, the Commission has raised awareness of local adult protection procedures, advised services of contact details and identified areas of training needs.

1.4 Understand the sources of support for the worker following disclosure or discovery of abuse

Abuse is devastating to those who suffer it and to those who are involved in identifying and dealing with it. It causes people to lose their self-esteem and confidence. Many children and adults become withdrawn and difficult to communicate with; anger is also a common response and may be directed at the abuser or at people around the victim.

This section will identify some of the support available to workers in the sector when they have been involved in an incident of abuse.

What you need to learn

- Support within the service setting.
- Support outside the service setting.
- Responding to abuse.
- Abuse procedures.

Care scenario: Healthcare Commission

In 2005, the Healthcare Commission and the Commission for Social Care Inspection looked at how services for people with a learning disability in Cornwall were being run.

They found that some people had been abused, for example one person at a hospital called Budock Hospital had been hurt more than once by another person with a learning disability and had a head injury. A person who lived in a supported-living house had been tied to their bed or wheelchair for about 16 hours a day.

The organisations looked at some standards called 'No Secrets'. The standards talked about how services could stop people being treated badly. When they looked at the services they found 40 cases where people were being badly treated or abused.

They also found that Cornwall Partnership NHS Trust and Cornwall Social Services were not dealing with these cases properly.

They found that people did not always get the right care and did not have enough choice or control over the care that they got. People who behaved in a difficult way were not treated in the right way by staff and some people did not have a plan to make sure they got the care and support they needed. In addition, some supported-living services were not properly registered: they were being run as care homes but were not on an official list.

These services did not meet the right standards of care. The investigators found that some supported-living services did not meet the standards of care that the Government talked about in a document called *Valuing People*.

Support within the service setting

Staff dealing with abusive situations will have different reactions. There is no right way to react, but each member of staff should have the opportunity to access support from their setting.

Supervision

National Minimum Standard for Care Homes for Older People 36.2 requires that:

- care staff receive formal supervision at least six times a year.

NMS 36.3 'Supervision' covers:

- all aspects of practice
- philosophy of care in the home
- career-development needs.

Supervision can take different forms:

- individual one-to-one meeting with staff
- a group supervision session
- perhaps observation of professional practice and a report and a record of the outcome.

Supervision is there as a support, not a challenge to practice.

Supervision is intended to be an on-going dialogue, on a one-to-one basis, which supports formal training, providing an opportunity to explain or discuss all aspects of the principles, objectives, policies and procedures of the setting. It is also a support mechanism, and a time to explore how a member of staff felt about a certain incident or procedure. Supervision is also intended to encourage a continuing learning environment within the setting. Often it may be useful for staff to access a mentor or other professional for support and supervision in relation to professional practice, building on the supervision provided.

The content of supervision sessions must be confidential, recorded only by the supervisee, but disclosure of information that contravenes the NMC or GSCC Codes of Conduct will be recorded by the manager and acted upon.

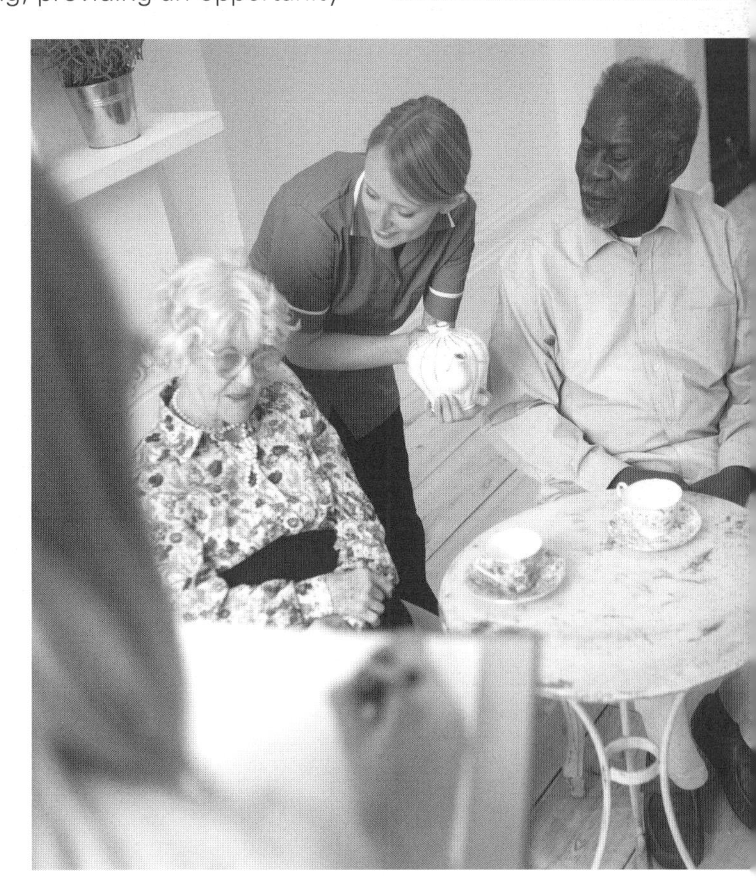

A care worker being supervised at work

Team support

It is important to work as a team. Staff in settings are one of the primary care providers for individuals in receipt of the service. The members of the team will vary depending on the size and organisational structure of the setting. At a very small care home, there may be only an administrator, a few direct care staff and the residents. Larger care homes may have directors, supervisors, specialists, housekeeping and nutrition staff as well as three shifts of direct care staff.

At the centre of the team is the individual and their preferences. The team, when it works together well, can provide better and more comprehensive care to an individual than staff members working separately.

In addition the team can support each other when abuse has taken place or been disclosed. This support can take the form of guidance or advice and support during work activities.

Activity 14

Think of a team. It could be a group to which you belong, a sports team on which your child plays or a team you see on TV.

What makes that team work well? Do they win, do something to help others, or simply complete what they set out to do?

Effective teams have the following positive aspects:

- they work towards a common goal
- they communicate well with each other
- they support one another
- they share responsibility
- they continually try to improve practice and service delivery.

Counselling

Counselling means different things to different people. It can describe anything from a cup of tea and a chat with a friend, to seeing a psychotherapist three times a week.

There are many times when we feel we need someone to listen to us, and want to be able to share our thoughts and feelings. This is essentially what counselling is. Being listened to can be really important if you have encountered incidents of abuse or have listened to a disclosure. You may be feeling angry, upset, and guilty at not identifying the risk, cross with the perpetrator or distressed that there is not more you can do for the individual concerned. All of these feelings are real and frightening, and can become overwhelming if they are not addressed.

Bottling feelings up can be draining and can make life difficult. Counselling provides an opportunity to explore your feelings and express them in a safe place. A counsellor can help you to find a way to make things less difficult to deal with.

'Counselling' generally means speaking to someone who is properly trained. This person may be called a counsellor or a psychotherapist. The difference between the two is sometimes difficult to identify, but the differences are usually to do with the kind of training and special interests of the individual counsellor or psychotherapist.

Look for local counselling provision in your area. Are there different types of counsellor? Do they work individually or is there a therapy centre?

Whether an individual sees a counsellor or a psychotherapist doesn't usually matter. What is important is that they have done the appropriate training and are properly accredited by a recognised organisation. Some other professionals (such as GPs, nurses, psychologists, psychiatrists and social workers) may have been trained in counselling as well, so it is always worth contacting your GP in the first instance. Often work settings have a service-level agreement with a local counsellor who can be accessed on a worker's behalf.

Training

As previously discussed, the General Social Care Council code of practice for social care workers describes the standards of professional conduct and practice required of social care workers as they carry out their job roles. This includes being accountable for the quality of your work and taking responsibility for maintaining and improving your knowledge and skills.

Think back to your induction. What were you told about, and how useful was this?

As a care worker it is important that you can contribute in a safe and appropriate manner to the work carried out in your care setting.

Induction is the way that your manager ensures that you can contribute to the quality of care that is provided, and that you do not make dangerous, or costly, mistakes that could put individuals at risk. Induction can have different meanings. It can involve a thorough programme of learning that takes place during

A training session

the first weeks of work. Alternatively, it can involve a learning programme of important basic skills and knowledge that takes place over a short period of time before a new job is started. Whichever approach is used, the manager is best placed to make sure induction is carried out properly. In a larger setting, the manager may delegate induction to a mentor to offer support during induction. The manager may also get some help from a trainer or a college for any specialist parts of induction, for example manual handling. The induction programme should be carried out within the first 12 weeks of employment, and must be based on the Skills for Care Common Induction Standards (2005) and the General Social Care Council Code of Practice (2002).

Look at the GSCC website and find the Codes of Practice. What are their key points?

The Skills for Care Common Induction Standards (2005) are a minimum standard for the induction of newly appointed staff in the care sector. There are six Common Induction Standards:

Standard 1: Understand the principles of care.
Standard 2: Understand the organisation and the role of the worker.
Standard 3: Maintain safety at work.
Standard 4: Communicate effectively.
Standard 5: Recognise and respond to abuse and neglect.
Standard 6: Develop as a worker.

Each main area has a set of outcomes that describe what must be done. Some of these units also cover parts of the NVQ in Health and Social Care.

Have a look at the Common Induction Standards on the Skills for Care website: www.skillsforcare.org.uk.

1. What topics do they cover?
2. Are they easy to understand?
3. Do you think they would be easy to work through?
4. Who would you ask for support or guidance with the Standards?

National Vocational Qualifications

The National Minimum Standards for Care Homes for Older People state that at least 50 per cent of care staff working in a care home will have achieved a Level 2 NVQ in Health and Social Care. In addition, your care home manager will probably have undertaken an NVQ Level 4 Registered Manager's Award, or equivalent.

An NVQ is an award that gives learners credit for what they do in their job every day. An NVQ is not like other qualifications that involve taking a course, or sitting a test or an examination, as you can use your performance at work as a basis for assessment. If you are competent in your job, you will complete an NVQ.

- How much training have you done?
- Does it meet your needs?
- Have you got more planned?

Care scenario: Natalia Beltsov

Natalia Beltsov is a part-time NVQ candidate with a local training provider. She is in her first month of working on her Health and Social Care NVQ Level 2.

Natalia says: 'I have wanted to work in health and social care for a long time, then when I came to England from Russia it seemed the right time to do this. I was told that I would need to be qualified and this would mean doing an NVQ. I was anxious about this as my English is very limited, but when I met my assessor, she was clear about what was expected of me, and told me that there would be support available for me to make sure I could complete my NVQ. I had had a bad experience at school in Russia and left early, but my assessor was not anything like the teachers there. If she sees that I am having trouble with a piece of work or with my English, she explains to me what I can do to improve rather than telling me off. I am really enjoying the NVQ course because I'm doing something I really want to do, and I really like my assessor. I can't wait to complete this Level 2 as my placement supervisor has said they will employ me full time when I have finished.'

Whether you are undertaking an induction programme or an NVQ, you will still need to develop your workplace knowledge and skills, and there are many courses available in order to help with this, for example: how to identify abuse or how to respond to a disclosure of abuse. Individual training needs may be identified and agreed during supervision sessions and included in a development plan. Completion of training offers staff the confidence and competence to deal with issues in a professional manner, ensuring the correct approach for the individual and the member of staff.

Training can also offer knowledge and insight into how to deal with incidents of abuse and the feelings that may accompany them.

Support outside the care setting

In addition to the support provided by work settings, there are also organisations and other individuals that can advise and offer guidance and support outside the setting. These include:

Using the Internet, library, newspapers or journals, look for other organisations that offer support to staff, carers and individuals involved in incidents of alleged or actual abuse. Examples include the Samaritans and GPs.

- Were they easy to find?
- Was the information provided useful?
- Were contact details provided if you wanted more information?

Action on Elder Abuse – this organisation operates at a number of different levels; it provides advice and guidance to older people and others through its helplines; it provides training to care staff and others, either as standard packages or specifically designed programmes; and it liaises with, challenges and supports regulators, care providers and Government. Support can also be provided for those who have been involved in reporting or dealing with incidents of abuse.

Crossroads – this organisation is about giving time and by doing this improving the lives of carers by giving them time to be themselves and have a break from their caring responsibilities. Its aim is to provide a reliable service, tailored to meet the individual needs of each carer and the person they are caring for. Crossroads has schemes in most parts of England and Wales, which provide a range of services to meet local needs.

Mental Health Care – this organisation offers support, advice and guidance to the carers of individuals with mental-health needs. This includes the opportunity to have a break, including the provision of personal care for half an hour to 24-hour holiday cover, a 24-hour helpline and friendship and support groups.

Those who carry out abuse can be anyone who is in a position of trust with an individual. This may include partners, children or other relatives, carers, friends or neighbours, volunteer workers, professional health care staff or residential care staff themselves. Care workers should monitor and notice when individuals are at risk from, or experiencing, neglect or abuse and respond appropriately to ensure that individuals are protected. The factors that are known to contribute to abuse and exploitation are shown in the diagram opposite.

Carrying out research at a library

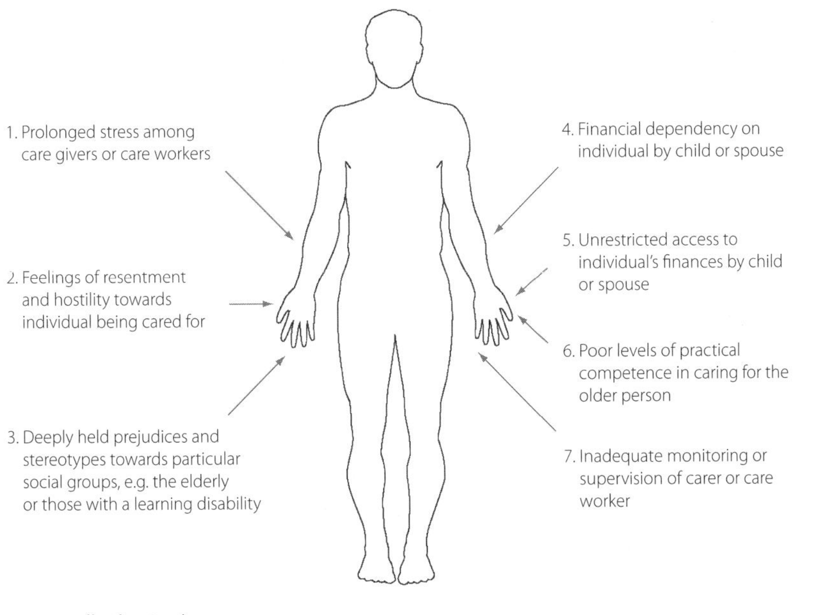

Factors contributing to abuse

Responding to abuse

Care scenario: Cornwall Partnership NHS Trust

In 2005, the Healthcare Commission notified the Secretary of State for Health that the early stages of the investigation had found significant failings in services. As a result, an outside team was brought in to urgently address these concerns while the investigation continued. The official investigation into learning disability services provided by Cornwall Partnership NHS Trust began in May 2005 and was sparked by concerns raised by East Cornwall Mencap Society.

The investigation also looked at two other treatment centres, four children's units and 46 houses occupied by groups of up to four people with learning disabilities. The report describes many years of abusive practices at the trust and the failure of senior trust executives to tackle this. Examples of abuse included physical abuse and misuse of people's money.

Investigators found evidence of institutional abuse, including some staff hitting, pushing, and dragging people. Some staff were also reported to have withheld food and given people cold showers.

A number of staff working in the homes were found to be caring and well intentioned. However, they were not working in accordance with best practice.

What do you think staff should have done differently?

The National Minimum Standards for Care Homes for Older People suggest that a four-stage approach to the problem of abuse should be applied, as follows:

1. **Prevention** – as far as is practical or possible, care homes need to aim at preventing abuse from happening at all.
2. **Identification** – where abuse does occur, homes need to identify it quickly and ensure that it is reported.
3. **Action** – once abuse has been identified, homes need to take swift action to deal with incidents and ensure the safety of their residents and service users.
4. **Planning** – homes need to use learning from incidents of abuse in their planning for the future.

The recommendations of the National Minimum Standards for Care Homes for Older People are explained in more detail below.

1. Prevention

How is abuse prevented in your setting? What actions are taken and do they work?

The best way of dealing with abuse is to prevent it from happening. Care homes should have policies and procedures in place, and should create a culture of awareness among care staff, including an understanding that abuse will not be tolerated in any way. The best way of ensuring that such a culture exists is through effective training, monitoring and supervision. Staff should be in no doubt that breaches of policy and procedures against abuse will be identified and dealt with immediately and effectively.

2. Identification

Would you know what to look for in your setting? Have you been trained in what to look for in relation to abuse?

Should it occur, it is vital that abuse is identified and reported. Staff should be trained to be aware of all forms of potential abuse and exploitation and should know exactly what to do and who to go to if they have any suspicions or concerns. This will include a need to support whistle-blowing. Very often staff can feel intimidated by abusers, especially if the abuser is a senior member of staff. There is also often a pressure to keep quiet and many are tempted to do this and ignore the abusive activity.

It is especially important that staff should be in no doubt that they will be supported by the work setting if they take the step of reporting abuse, and that to keep quiet about an abusive situation may in itself be viewed as a disciplinary or even criminal act.

What does *whistle-blowing* mean? Look for a definition of it.

3. Action

Any report or suggestion of abuse, no matter how minor, should be taken seriously, immediately investigated and the appropriate action taken. These investigations should be fair and transparent and, if staff are involved, carried out following employment law and organisational policy. The consent or co-operation of the victim to an investigation is an important aspect in any action taken, and trust is often a key element in obtaining that consent. Often the victims of abuse feel intimidated to keep silent or fear the repercussions of speaking out. They may also feel confused or unworthy and not know who to trust, so mechanisms to support this are very important.

Have you or has anyone you know ever been involved in taking action in relation to a case of abuse?

4. Planning

It is vital that care organisations learn from incidents of abuse and that this is included in the way they operate in the future. Obvious examples of where this may be especially effective are in improvements to staff training or the use of advocacy services.

Abuse procedures

Ask to see a copy of your setting's procedure in the event of an incident of abuse. Is it easy to access and understand?

According to the National Minimum Standards for Care Homes for Older People, the immediate safety or health of the victim is the first concern. Staff should talk to the victim and assess the situation, summoning help, giving first aid and calling for medical support, an ambulance or the Police as necessary. If the abuser is still present, staff should attempt to calm the situation, but should not place themselves at risk.

If the situation is not an emergency, all suspicions and events should be reported to the person in charge so they can take appropriate action.

Confidentiality

Tact and sensitivity are important in this process and it may sometimes be necessary for a member of staff known to the individual to talk to them rather than the person in charge. In situations where the individual says that they will tell a member of staff but asks that member of staff not to tell anyone else, the care worker should advise the individual that they cannot keep that confidentiality and must by policy inform the manager or person in charge. However, they should reassure the victim that their information will be treated as confidential and that the home will not necessarily proceed with an investigation without their consent unless there has been a criminal act and the law has been broken, or unless the alleged abuse involves others at risk.

Consent

consent
agreement or acceptance

Consent is an important consideration. In general, the victims of abuse do not have to take action against their abuser and have the right not to. This is particularly common where the abuser may be a son or a daughter or another member of the family. If the suspected victim does not want the incident to be taken further, their wishes must be respected unless the victim is:

- in physical danger
- clearly incapable of making an informed decision themselves, therefore requiring further assessment
- not the only person at risk or involved.

Consider how you would feel about dealing with such an incident. Who might you want to talk to afterwards to help you deal with your feelings?

The underlying principle here is that a person has the right to decide how they want to be helped – or if they want to be helped at all. Where an individual is considered incapable of making an informed decision or of giving consent, the person in charge should discuss the situation with close relatives or guardians. Possible risks and outcomes need to be explained carefully to the individual so that an informed decision can be made.

It must also be remembered that if an issue is not dealt with the abuser is then free to carry out abuse or harm again. If abuse is dealt with by an organisation, the POVA procedure is enforced and the individual will not be able to work in the sector again.

All cases of abuse where the victim gives consent for action to be taken, should be referred to social services or CSCI without delay. In situations where there is evidence of a criminal act, the case should be reported immediately to the Police by the manager or person in charge. This is particularly important in suspected sexual abuse, where the police will want to gather evidence as quickly as possible. Referral to the police or social services should include the following information:

- personal details of the victim
- the referrer's details
- the substance of the allegation
- details of the alleged abuser
- details of specific incidents or events including dates, places, injuries, witnesses, etc.
- whether or not consent has been given to take the matter further.

Look up the Data Protection Act 1998. How would it apply when a referral has been made?

Recording the facts

Once a referral has been made, social services will work to their own guidelines and procedures and staff should always co-operate. All facts, incidents, assessments and discussions related to the suspicions should be recorded clearly and accurately in the individual's plan of care as soon after the incident as possible. These records are strictly confidential and should be kept securely and safely according to the Data Protection Act 1998, as they may be used as evidence in a future criminal investigation.

Action

Where no referral to social services is made, in line with the victim's wishes, alternative courses of action should be considered and the individual given appropriate support. If the alleged abuser is a member of staff, the home should proceed with disciplinary action and an internal investigation in line with the home's disciplinary policy. The action of the staff member may constitute grounds for dismissal through gross misconduct, even if no criminal case is pursued. Careful notes should be kept, outlining the exact suspicions and the action taken. In the case of a relative or carer being the alleged abuser, the home may arrange with the individual to restrict visits or to have only accompanied visits. In all instances, the situation should be carefully monitored.

Homes must also be prepared to accept that in some cases of abuse little action can be taken beyond continued support, recording and monitoring, due to limitations in the law and the victim not wanting to proceed. However, in all cases detailed written records should be kept in a secure place and all staff should work together to minimise the risk of further abuse.

The Police have a duty to investigate any possible criminal offences, which will include interviewing victims, witnesses and suspects and gathering evidence. This process may not always end in criminal proceedings, but early involvement will give the Police the best opportunity to conduct their investigations effectively. Cases of suspected sexual abuse should always be reported to the police immediately.

A police officer carrying out an interview

1. People who are dependent on others for their care needs are vulnerable to abuse and exploitation.
2. Abuse often arises as a result of an imbalance of power between the individual and care giver.
3. Individuals may suffer from a number of different types of abuse, neglect and exploitation. These might include physical, sexual, financial or emotional abuse.
4. Be aware of the signs and symptoms of abuse.
5. Always follow the policies and procedures of your care setting when responding to any concerns about abuse, neglect or exploitation.
6. Any concerns regarding suspected or alleged abuse or neglect must be reported to a supervisor or senior manager immediately.
7. The issue of individual consent is important in any investigation of alleged abuse or exploitation.
8. Care workers must ensure that allegations of abuse or exploitation are handled sensitively and in a confidential manner.

2 Danger, harm and abuse

2.1 Understand the different types of abuse/harm

In this section you will learn about the different forms that abuse can take and why it is important to be aware of the indications and signs that abuse or harm has been carried out. You will also learn about what might lead to harm or abuse being carried out and the effects it has on individuals. It is also important to remember that noticing signs or symptoms may not necessarily mean that abuse has taken place.

What you need to learn

- Types of abuse.

Types of abuse

Physical abuse

This is probably one of the most common forms of abuse that happens in the care sector. It can take many forms including hitting, slapping, burning, pushing or restraining. Rough or careless handling may also be seen as physical harm, as can giving too much medication or the wrong type of medication. Neglect may also occur when there are resource or staffing shortages and the appropriate care is not provided. While this may not be intentional, it can still result in harm or abuse through the lack of medical care or attention.

Neglect/acts of omission

These are another kind of abuse that can take many forms and can occur when an individual is not provided with adequate care or attention and suffers harm or distress as a result. Examples are where an individual is deprived of food, water, heat, clothing, comfort or essential medication.

Neglect may also occur when there are resource or staffing shortages and the appropriate care is not provided. This may not be intentional, but can still result in harm or abuse through lack of medical care or attention.

Financial/material

This is most commonly the obtaining of money, valuable possessions or property through cheating, theft or deception and is thought by many to be a growing problem amongst vulnerable adults.

Psychological

This can be a more difficult area to detect and identify. Generally it is viewed as cruelty or verbal insults, but it can include shouting, swearing, blaming, ignoring, bullying or humiliating a person. The spreading of rumours or malicious gossip is also viewed as abuse. Everyone should be able to live with privacy, dignity, independence and choice and all information about them should remain confidential. Therefore a breach of confidentiality may well be considered psychological or emotional abuse. However, if a member of staff breaches confidentiality, does this immediately become an incident of abuse? It may have been done by mistake or because the member of staff thought a third party had a right to know the information.

Sexual

This most obviously occurs wherever an individual is forced to take part in any sexual activity without their permission or consent. However, sexual abuse can also take more subtle forms and any sexual relationship between staff and individuals can be considered to be abusive, even if it is consensual. Sexual abuse may also occur when staff are administering personal care to an individual.

Institutional

This takes the form of repeated instances of poor care of individuals or groups of individuals. It can often be through neglect or poor professional practice as a result of structures, policies, processes and practices within an organisation. While not suggesting that this action is correct, it is important to recognise the powerful influence that organisational culture has on individual behaviour.

institutional abuse
neglect or a routine that offers little or no choice

discriminatory abuse
unfair treatment of an individual, treating them less well than others, using any difference there may be as a reason

Discriminatory

Discrimination that is carried out on grounds that include sex, race, colour, language, culture, religion, politics or sexual orientation. It is a form of discrimination based on a person's disability or age and can include harassment, degrading slurs and hate crimes.

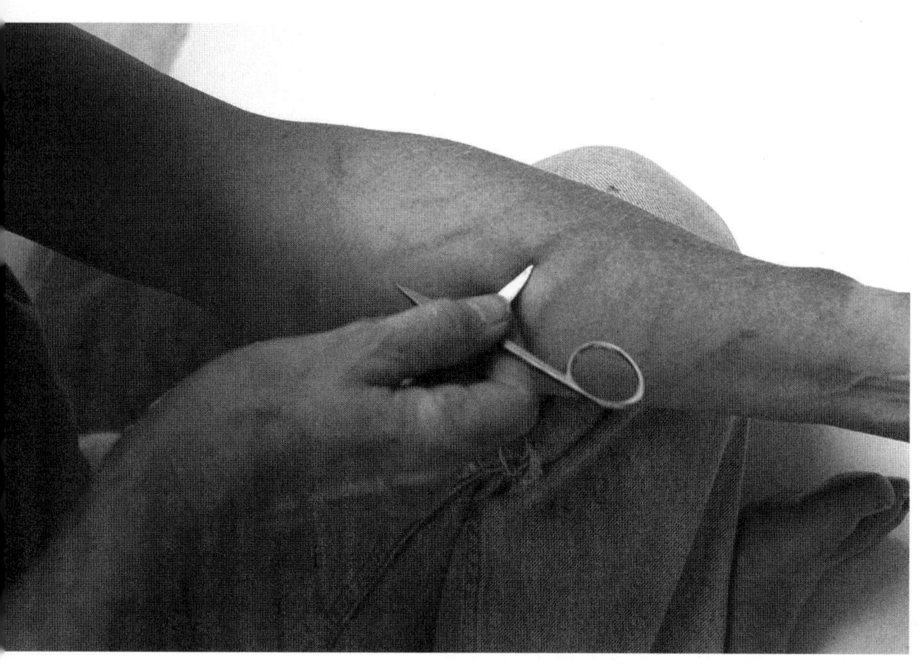

Self-harm

Self-harm/abuse

Self-harm or abuse is the attempt to deliberately cause harm to one's own body and the injury is usually severe enough to cause tissue damage. The most common form is superficial and usually involves cutting, burning, pulling of hair, the breaking of bones, hitting, picking at wounds that are healing and any other method used to harm oneself.

Some people believe that another form of abuse is that of generally abusive regimes. Such regimes are characterised by a lack of concern or even contempt for individuals, a lack of flexibility or choice, a lack of privacy, a lack of respect, public discussion of matters private to individuals, unjustified use of restraints, staff using master keys to enter rooms without due cause and generally restrictive practices full of petty rules and restrictions.

Activity 15

Draw a line to link the type of abuse to the actions that might take place for each one.

Physical	Carers fail to meet individual's needs for basic necessities such as food, shelter, clothing or medical care.
Sexual	Individuals may be harmed by ignoring them, by belittling them or through name-calling.
Emotional	Individuals are hurt, leaving marks such as bruises in places where they would not occur in normal activities.
Neglect	Harmful behaviour by other individuals that makes a person fearful.
Bullying	Individuals experience inappropriate contact with others.

Abuse is something done by one person to another, without their full understanding or consent, that harms or distresses them in some way. An abused individual may be:

- in need of help because of a disability or illness
- unable to take care of themselves
- unable to stop someone else from harming or exploiting them.

This section explores who may be at risk and why. It is also important to remember that an individual may belong to more than one of these groups, and assessment should reflect this.

What you need to learn

- Groups at high risk of abuse.

Groups at high risk of abuse

Lacking mental awareness and capacity

Individuals with mental-health problems often have greater dependency needs and more limited methods of communication, making them more vulnerable. Often an individual is unable to choose to stop the abuse, due to their lack of understanding of what is happening, or it may be that the fear of telling the abuser to stop what they are doing, creates a pressure that they cannot overcome. In addition there may be a need for acceptance from the abuser or they may be dependent on the abuser.

People with limited awareness or capacity often do not realise that what is happening is abusive, nor do they know it is illegal. As a result they may never tell anyone about potentially or actual abusive situations.

Individuals with greater awareness are often frightened to talk openly about such experiences, due to the risk of not being believed or taken seriously. It may be even more difficult for people with limited awareness to report abuse, since they are typically told and taught not to question carers or others in authority.

Severely physically disabled

Individuals with severe physical disabilities are not often taught or informed about abusive issues. Or they may not be given assertiveness training, which is necessary to enable them to know the difference between safe and not-so-safe people and situations, and in knowing how to say no to unwanted sexual propositions or other advances. Often they think they do not have the right or the ability to refuse abusive treatment, particularly if the abuser is an authority figure, such as a parent, relative, worker or some other individual who is respected by other family members, neighbours and colleagues.

Think about the support that could be given to individuals with a sensory impairment to ensure they can make the choices and decisions they would like to, for example an interpreter can help with communication.

Sensory impaired

Individuals with a sensory impairment are often hindered by speech impediments, limited hearing or vision or a restricted vocabulary. There may be additional problems with difficulties in reading and writing.

There are many reasons to suggest that individuals with sensory impairments will be more susceptible to abuse than other people. Individuals with sensory impairments are often cared for by, and in contact with, carers who may be potential abusers. In addition, some potential abusers will seek an individual who appears vulnerable, more limited in their communication abilities, who demonstrates a need for contact, and who either will not tell of the act or who would probably not be believed if they did. Individuals are often placed in a vulnerable situation, cared for on a one-to-one basis with sometimes very limited contact with others.

Semi-comatose/comatose

Being semi-conscious or unconscious carries similar risks to those of individuals with physical or sensory impairments or disabilities. The individual is not able to protect themselves or to speak up for themselves. This semi-conscious or comatose condition may be due to illness, accident or misuse of drugs or alcohol.

A person with a visual impairment, with a guide dog

In order to reduce incidents of harm or abuse, staffing recruitment, retention, skills mix and training are important to make sure that effective monitoring is carried out and that reporting systems are reliable.

How could you make sure that an individual who was unconscious was safe and not at risk?

Aphasic

Aphasia is a language disorder that results from damage to the parts of the brain that control language. For most individuals, these are on the left side (hemisphere) of the brain. Aphasia usually occurs suddenly, often as the result of a stroke or head injury, but it may also develop slowly, for example in the case of an individual with a brain tumour.

The disorder affects the expression and understanding of language as well as reading and writing. The risks to an individual with aphasia are similar to those for an individual with a sensory impairment. Limited communication means that there is a limited information exchange.

There are many signs that may indicate that abuse is being carried out and this section discusses possible signs that abuse may be occurring. However it is important to remember that this is not a complete list and that other signs and symptoms might also exist. It is also important to remember that noticing one or more of these signs does not in itself mean that abuse is being carried out; it may indicate that abuse is a possibility. In this section you will learn why it is important to know what to look for.

What you need to learn

- Why knowledge of the signs and symptoms is important.
- Common indicators of abuse by type.

Activity 16

In each row, write two possible signs or symptoms of abuse.

Type of abuse	Sign/symptom	Sign/symptom
Physical		
Psychological		
Neglect/acts of omission		
Financial/material		
Institutional		
Self-harm/abuse		
Sexual		

Why knowledge of the signs and symptoms is important

Often victims of abuse or neglect are afraid to speak out because the person who is abusing them is also providing their care, or may be a close relative or friend. That is why it is so important to be on the lookout for signs of abuse. But do remember, it is not your responsibility to prove abuse or neglect, but it is your responsibility as a worker to report any concerns so that they can be evaluated or investigated by professionals.

You should also remember, as stated earlier, that what might look like a sign of abuse or neglect may not be, so further investigation by a senior member of staff may be necessary. It is also important to remember that those who carry out abuse can be very clever in hiding the injuries they have caused. For example, a bruise or cut may be explained as self-harm or a fall while getting out of the bath.

Common indicators of abuse by type

Physical abuse

This is the use of physical force against someone in a way that injures them or puts them in danger. There is a broad range of behaviours that fall under the heading of physical abuse, including hitting, grabbing, choking, throwing things, and assault with a weapon. These actions can lead to some obvious signs being observable, including:

- unexplained bruises or cuts, especially where they reflect the shape of an object used, of a hand or of finger marks
- loss of hair in clumps or abrasions on the scalp from hair-pulling
- unexplained fractures
- unexplained burns, bites or scalding
- delays in reporting injuries
- cowering or flinching when approached
- vague, implausible or inappropriate explanations
- multiple injuries or a history of injuries, particularly falls.

Psychological abuse

We may often think that physical abuse is far worse than emotional or psychological abuse, since physical violence can send a person to hospital and leave them with scars. But the scars of emotional abuse can be very deep and real to the individual involved. In fact, emotional abuse can be just as damaging as physical abuse – at times even more so. In addition, emotional abuse can worsen over time, often escalating to physical abuse. This type of abuse can result in some of the following signs and symptoms:

- fearfulness
- mood changes including depression, irritability and unhappiness
- low self-esteem
- an individual's responses to others

- an unwillingness to make eye contact
- incontinence
- changes in sleep and appetite patterns
- withdrawn, self-isolating behaviour.

Neglect/acts of omission

Neglect is a continued lack of appropriate care for individuals, including the provision of safety, nourishment, warmth and medical attention. This can have a serious effect on an individual's mental and emotional development. Examples of signs and symptoms of neglect or acts of omission are:

- debilitation or weakness through malnutrition or dehydration
- unexplained weight loss
- poor hygiene and unkempt, dirty appearance, clothes or surroundings
- inappropriate dress
- lack of aids/treatment to support life
- pressure sores
- poor skin condition and limited resistance to infection and disease.

over-medicating
giving an individual additional medication to keep them quiet or calm so that they will be less trouble

Over-medicating, though the opposite of neglect, is still classified as abuse. It may be the case, for example, that additional medication is given to keep an individual quiet or calm to give a carer or carers some peace.

Financial/material

Financial abuse occurs when a person or persons take advantage of someone financially. This includes stealing money, lying about how much the individual may need for certain care, or cashing the individual's cheques without permission. Any of these actions can lead to the following symptoms:

- going without basic necessities (food, clothes, medication, shelter)
- unexplained loss of money or inability to pay bills
- sudden withdrawals of money
- sudden disappearance of favourite or valuable possessions
- loss of financial documents such as pension books, building-society books, etc.

Institutional

Institutional abuse of vulnerable people can take place in hospitals and care homes as well as in domestic settings. If this type of abuse is carried out, many signs and symptoms can be observed. However, these may be indicators that other forms of abuse are being carried out, or may simply be how the individual is responding to being in a care setting, so caution must be taken. Indicators of institutional abuse may be:

- treating adults like children
- individuals flinching from staff
- decisions made only by the staff group, service or organisation
- strict, regimented routines for daily activities such as mealtimes, bedtimes, bathing, washing and going to the toilet
- loss of dignity
- ill health due to limited care provision
- drowsiness as a result of ill health and poor care
- lack of cleanliness resulting in an unkempt appearance
- little choice in areas such as food and drink, dress, daily and social activities
- lack of privacy, dignity, choice or respect for individuals
- lack of support for dress, diet or religious observance in accordance with an individual's belief or cultural background
- withdrawing people from their valued community or family contact.

Self harm/abuse

Self-harm or abuse can take several forms, this includes cutting or injuring various parts of the body, often the forearms or legs; taking pills and burning. Indicators that this has been happening include:

- unexplained cuts, bites, scratches, bruises or fractures
- hair loss
- indicators of substance misuse
- the wearing of long sleeves or trousers to hide cuts or bruises
- wounds that will not heal.

If you notice signs of abuse, you should alert your senior or manager

It is important to pass on any concerns or things that you have noticed to your senior or manager. They may or may not be an indicator of abuse, but it is important to tell someone.

Sexual

Any situation in which an individual is forced to participate in degrading sexual activity is sexual abuse. Such actions can result in a variety of signs or symptoms, and these can include:

- unexplained difficulty walking
- attention-seeking
- overt sexual behaviour
- reluctance to undress or remove any clothing
- infection of genital area
- bleeding or bruised genitals
- reluctance to be alone with a particular person
- sudden behaviour change.

2.4 Understand the factors that can affect the individual, carer or social care worker that may lead to harm or abuse

Issues that may impact on incidents of abuse include low staffing levels, a lack of training, lack of management or leadership or an organisation that is part of a culture that is closed to other ideas, for example a care setting where new ideas, visitors, care management or other professional involvement are not encouraged.

There are other factors that can make an individual more vulnerable to abuse or make an individual abuse or harm someone.

What you need to learn

- Factors that lead to harm or abuse.

Factors that lead to harm or abuse

Stress and anxiety

While stress is a commonly used excuse for abuse, it does not itself cause abuse. We all experience stress, but most stressed people do not hurt others and most abusers under stress do not hit their managers or colleagues; they choose victims who have less power, such as family members or those they provide care for.

Providing care for an unwell or immobile person can be stressful at times. Carers may say that their behaviour is due to the stress of providing care because they are overwhelmed by the demands of this role. Stress can potentially lead to physical, psychological or sexual abuse being carried out, or it may be that other actions are carried out and abuse is not limited to the types mentioned.

Illness

People with a mental illness can experience problems in the way they think, feel or behave. This can significantly affect their relationships, their work, their social life and their quality of life. Having a mental illness is difficult, not only for the individual concerned, but also for their family and friends. Some mental illnesses, for example schizophrenia, may have challenging or violent behaviours as one of their symptoms.

Some medical conditions or combinations of medications may cause a normally calm person to become aggressive or violent. It may not be the medical condition itself but the anxiety connected with being ill or the restrictions it brings which cause aggression and potential abuse, perhaps in the form of physical or psychological abuse. But it is important to be aware that some abusers use mental or physical illness as an excuse to continue with their abusive behaviour, not asking for help or support.

Sleep deprivation

How many times have we all said that we need more sleep? It seems the busier we are and the more tired we get, the more difficult it can be to get a good night's sleep. It's not just about being tired and groggy the next day: lack of sleep can result in memory loss, poor decision-making, reduced energy levels, accidents, depression and mood swings.

The frontal cortex of the brain needs adequate sleep in order to function effectively. Without sufficient sleep, tasks such as thinking, remembering things and solving problems may be affected. This can result in a short temper, leading to potential abuse.

Activity 17

Think about a time when you did not have enough sleep.

1. How did you feel?
2. Could you still make important decisions?
3. How do you think these feelings could lead to an individual being abusive to others?

Carers should ensure that they get sufficient sleep and rest in order to carry out their responsibilities. If they do not, abuse may result, such as neglect due to lack of energy or time to give.

Effects of substance misuse

Many people use drugs or alcohol and are never abusive, and drugs and alcohol on their own are not the cause of abuse or violence. However, the violence may get worse when an individual uses drugs or alcohol. Often, abusers will use drugs or alcohol as an excuse for their violent or abusive behaviour.

Abusers who are addicted to drugs or alcohol have two separate issues to address: abusive behaviour and substance abuse. Alcohol and drug treatment programmes are designed to help an individual stay sober, not to prevent the abusive behaviour.

Learned behaviours

Abusive parents can unknowingly teach children that abuse is a good way to control another individual. To carry out abuse is a choice: individuals who grew up with abuse can choose to behave abusively or they can choose to stop the pattern of violence that they are familiar with. Many adults who were victims of abuse or witnessed domestic violence while they were growing up, have healthy and happy adult relationships and do not hurt their children, partners or parents.

Some individuals who were abused as children experience emotional problems or mental illness as adults, often as a result of this abuse. This may require specific treatment to deal with the effects of what happened, however, this is not an excuse for abusive behaviour.

What support is available for individuals who have been victims of abuse, either recently or when they were younger? One example is the Samaritans. Can you think of others?

Lack of support and guidance

Lack of social or care support or advice and guidance can lead to abuse, for example a lack of information or direction can result in unintentional neglect: the carer is not aware of the particular needs of individuals, so does not provide them. If an individual requires medication at a very specific time then it must be dispensed according to instructions, not doing this could potentially cause further illness or upset.

Caring is a demanding task, and carers can easily neglect their own health and well-being, so it is important to realise that they need time off from their responsibilities to relieve stress, tiredness and prevent burnout. Effective, sustainable caring depends on meeting the carer's own needs for reassurance, support and periodic respite.

Respite care provides time off for family members, volunteers or carers who care for someone who is ill, injured or frail. It can take place in an adult day centre, in the home of the individual being cared for, or even in a residential setting such as respite care or a nursing home. Although there are different approaches to respite care, they all have the same basic objective: to provide carers with temporary, intermittent support, on a planned basis, to give them a break from the daily responsibilities of caring.

Resolutions for lack of support or guidance include making health care and support more accessible and affordable, expanding and improving the coordination of social services, and ensuring that the needs of the individual and carers are met as far as possible. Also important is encouraging carers to identify their needs and to feel confident in asking for help when they need it, rather than feeling guilty.

Lack of training (social care worker)

Similar to a lack of support and guidance, unintentional neglect may result from lack of appropriate or adequate training about how to provide care or because staff members cannot monitor individuals in an effective manner. Adequate training is vital if carers are to deliver care in an efficient and appropriate manner. Lack of training is the source of a large range of potential problems, from incorrect transfers to bathing accidents. Carers should be trained in dealing with situations that can lead to harm or abuse. The organisation or setting may have provided training and have on-going monitoring or training in place, but part of the role of the senior or supervisory staff is to help carers work to best practice and implement their training. Another role is to ensure that safe procedures are adhered to. Without adequate supervision, carers may use inappropriate measures or techniques, to the detriment of patient care.

Lack of employment and finances

Being unemployed can make a carer feel undervalued and worthless; this in turn allows little money to pay for care and expenses. As a result, tempers can be frayed and the level of anxiety high. The individual receiving care may be seen as a burden or a drain on already limited resources, raising concerns about finances and the future. Abuse or neglect can result. Additional support can help to ease the situation; the provision or offer of respite care or ensuring that all benefits are being claimed should offer valuable help.

Shortage of money can cause stress, and may lead to abuse or neglect

Individuals can experience several different kinds of harm or abuse from people they rely on or trust. Abuse and neglect can affect an individual's health, happiness and safety. In this section you will learn about the impact of abuse on people and how it affects their self-esteem and behaviour.

What you need to learn

- Common effects of abuse.

Common effects of abuse

Lack of confidence, self-esteem and anxiety

People often experience worry, depression, or anxiety as a result of abuse and neglect; some people may mistake these for signs of memory loss or illness, when really they are the impact of stress or worry. An older adult may feel shame, guilt, or embarrassment that someone in the family or someone close has harmed them. An older adult who feels abused or neglected usually loses trust in the person who causes the harm. Sometimes when older adults tell someone about the abuse, the person hearing it might act as if they do not believe them. This can cause further harm to the person's feelings.

Some older adults who have experienced abuse earlier or throughout their lives may use alcohol or prescription drugs to help with sleeping difficulties or anxiety; this is their way of coping with the emotional and physical hurt. In extreme circumstances some individuals may develop a dependency on alcohol or medication.

Withdrawal or depression

For some people, withdrawal or depression as a result of abuse can be intense and may last for weeks at a time. For others depression can be less severe but may linger at a lower level for years. Depression is a strong feeling of sadness, despair, or hopelessness that can last for weeks, months, or even longer. Depression interferes with an individual's ability to take part in normal activities, resulting in withdrawal. Symptoms may include:

- low mood or sadness much of the time
- lack of energy
- withdrawal from friends and family
- significant weight change

- change in sleep pattern
- feelings of guilt or worthlessness
- thoughts of death or suicide.

Activity 18

Alison has been a care worker in a residential setting for adults with physical disabilities for the past two years. Alison enjoys her job but fears that residents could easily be taken advantage of. Regular lunchtimes have become routine and no choices are offered. Staff plan activities for the evenings, selecting activities they think residents would like. This has been carried out for years and no one has ever complained, so the staff assume that everyone is happy with the arrangements.

1. Do you think everyone really is happy with the arrangements?
2. What changes do you think the staff could make?
3. Are Alison and the other staff working to best practice?

Subservient behaviour

When individuals are in fear of other people they may behave differently; abuse and violence have a huge impact over time and the fear, pain, and stress are reflected. Abusers may become overly dependent on their partners for their unmet emotional needs, expecting that the partner's behaviour and attitude meet their demanding needs. Abusers often use subtle forms of abuse to punish, humiliate, and control their partners.

Consistent seeking of approval

The attachment of individuals to their abusers is common, and happens in many controlling relationships.

By creating a false emotional attachment and seeking praise and approval from their abuser, the abused individual attempts to create a false relationship in which no harm can come to them. And by defending or protecting their abuser from the Police or anyone who wants to help or intervene, they allow themselves to appear as if they have some control in a relationship where they really have none.

Anger, aggression or abusive behaviour

We all feel hurt or angry when someone or something obstructs our needs or plans, and anger commonly develops following abuse. Anger is a healthy and common reaction, but only as long as it is not aimed at themselves. Anger can be a helpful tool for regaining the strength and the courage needed to regain control of their life. The abused person may also feel anger towards society and the legal system for allowing the abuse to happen, and towards significant others for not understanding what has happened. Anger is particularly and understandably aimed at the abuser and also at the disruption in their life caused by the incidents.

Aggression takes anger a step further. Aggression is a behaviour that is intended to cause harm or even pain. It could be in the form of verbal or even physical assaults, property damage or any kind of destructive behaviour.

An abused person may direct their aggressive behaviour at themselves in the form of self-harm or abuse. This is their way of expressing their anger and anxiety at what has happened and acts as a release for their emotional tensions and anxieties.

Look up definitions of the following terms:

- anger
- aggression
- self-esteem
- subservient behaviour
- depression.

Anger is a common reaction to abuse

3 Social norms, values and perceptions

3.1 Understand the factors that affect the development of values and social norms, both for service users and for workers

Sometimes the norms and values of the workplace conflict with those of the individual, such as when a member of staff takes a full hour for lunch to go shopping but the rest of the staff, including the manager, regularly work through the lunch hour. This can also happen in relation to the needs of the individual receiving care, and care needs to be taken when making decisions to ensure that situations are not prejudged. For example, an individual may choose to dress in summer clothes during the cold winter months. Who are we to judge this, when the individual is perfectly able to make their own decisions?

This section also looks at the impact social norms have on behaviours. Assessment of need should consider the context of these norms and behaviours and the impact they have on assessments and service provision. It is also important to be aware of the dilemmas and challenges which could be faced when providing care.

What you need to learn

- Parenting styles (permissive, authoritative, authoritarian).
- Family dynamics (extended family, lone parenting, isolated family, same-gender family grouping).
- Class and cultural variations (status, wealth, beliefs).
- Education (formal, informal).
- Life experiences (history, illness, trauma, employment).

Parenting styles

As all parents know all too well, parenting is complex, and there are no easy answers. The interaction of many actions and attitudes on the part of parents come together to impact on a child's development. 'Parenting style' refers to the broad overall pattern of parental actions, rather than to a single act.

Permissive parenting

Permissive, or indulgent, parenting involves being accepting and warm but exerting little control. Permissive parents do not set limits, allowing children to set their own rules, schedules and activities. They do not demand the same high levels of behaviour as authoritarian or authoritative parents.

Authoritative parenting

Authoritative, or moderate, parents set limits and rely on naturally occurring risks or consequences for children to learn from making their own mistakes. Authoritative parents explain to their children why rules are important and why they must be followed. They reason with their children and consider the children's point of view even though they might not agree. They are firm, but show kindness, warmth and love. Authoritative parents set high standards and encourage children to be independent.

Authoritarian parenting

Authoritarian, or extremely strict, parents are highly controlling. They dictate how their children should behave. They stress obedience to authority and discourage discussion. They are demanding and directive. They expect their orders to be obeyed and do not encourage give-and-take. They have low levels of sensitivity and do not expect their children to disagree with their decisions.

authoritarian
where the parents are in charge and children do as they are told

It has been identified that the best-adjusted children, particularly in terms of social competence, had parents with an authoritative and moderate parenting style. These parents are able to balance identified high demands with emotional responsiveness and respect for their child's autonomy and choice. Children of overly strict parents are apt to be reliant on the voice of authority and to be lacking in spontaneity. In contrast, the authoritative parent permits the child enough freedom of expression to develop a sense of independence. Permissive parents make few demands, and children have been found to have difficulty controlling their impulses; they are immature and often reluctant to accept responsibility.

Family dynamics

Family culture is our set of beliefs about how things should be. It identifies things like who is the boss, who does what work around the house and roles for men and women. In addition to this, every family has its own way of relating to each other, this is known as family dynamics. Dynamics are influenced by things like the structure of the family; the numbers of children and adults and how they are related and the personalities of each family member, cultural background, values, and personal or family experiences.

dynamics
how groups, families or individuals communicate, work, socialise or co-exist together

As a care worker, do you get to meet the families of the individuals you provide care for? What level of input into care provision do they have?

An extended family is two or more adults from different generations of a family, who share a household. The family may consist of more than just parents and children; it may include parents, children, cousins, aunts, uncles, grandparents and foster children. The extended family may live together for many reasons, to help raise children, to support an ill relative, or to help with financial problems. Sometimes children are raised by their grandparents when their biological parents have died or can no longer take care of them. Many grandparents take some primary responsibility for childcare, particularly when both parents work.

A single parent bringing up a child or children is often referred to as 'lone parenting'. The frustration of being a single parent can create stress and anxiety levels that can be harmful to the parent and their child or children; left unchecked this can lead at worst to harm or abuse, neglect or a breakdown of emotions. Children could be guided by the views of the parent they spend the majority of their time with, perhaps not always getting the benefit or balance of a two-parent view. However, many children develop and flourish as a result of living with one parent.

An isolated family may be one that is in social or demographic isolation and does not encourage interaction or communication with others. This does not offer the wealth of socialisation that can come with interaction or encourage the development of social or communication skills. Children in this situation are only aware of their small microcosm of life and not of the activities of other families and friends.

Same-sex marriage is a term for a socially or religiously recognised marriage in which two people of the same sex live together as a family, with children from either partner.

Activity 19

Take a look around you: what types of families do you see? There are many variations in our local communities. Make a note of what you have observed.

Class and cultural variations

Social status is the honour attached to an individual's position in society: social position. Social status is generally determined in two ways. An individual or family can earn their social status by their own achievements (achieved status), or can be placed in the stratification, or class, system by their inherited position (ascribed status). There is also economic status, where an individual's position in the stratification structure is based on their wealth, education, and occupation. It is also important to think about inherited wealth, savings, occupational benefits, and ownership of homes or land.

We all have our own system of beliefs, which influences our perceptions of what is real and our assessment of ourselves. Wealth and status can impact on our belief systems; for example we may think that everyone lives in the same way and to the same standard as we do.

Education

Formal education is classroom-, college- or university-based, provided by trained teachers, tutors, assessors or lecturers. Informal education happens outside the classroom, in after-school programmes, work-based learning, community-based organisations or at home.

The impact of education on how we see the world and our values is huge. What we learn directs our knowledge and informs our thinking. Lack of education can have the opposite effect, offering individuals little insight or experience into what is morally right or wrong. This can impact on the abuser or the abused, with little knowledge or experience of what is right or wrong to guide their actions.

Where did you go to school or college? Was it the same place as your colleagues?

At school

Life experiences

Life experiences can include losing a job, problems with money, the death of a loved one, illness, divorce, abuse, having and bringing up children, work achievements, educational achievements or any other aspect of life that has had a profound impact.

People handle these events in different ways. It all depends on the type of person you are, your genetic make-up, and how much support you have had during your life and its experiences. But these events can shape how individuals, both abusers and the abused, see and understand values and norms. For example, if an abusive relationship is all an individual knows, then they accept it, since they know no differently. In addition it may, for them, be acceptable to continue this cycle of abuse and harm.

3.2 Understand how the points in 3.1 influence how situations may be perceived as abusive or protective

In this section you will learn about how different people may see different situations.

What you need to learn

How different people view incidents:

- the individual
- family and friends
- social care workers.

The individual

How an individual views incidents of abuse and how they are protected from them may vary according to their culture, knowledge or earlier experiences. They may think that any restrictions placed upon them limit their choice, so it will need to be clearly explained to them that this is for their own benefit and to reduce the risk of harm or abuse.

When we are younger our upbringing may seem restrictive and we might try to rebel against it. But in the main it is for our own good and for our safety. This also applies to the way a family lives, socialises and communicates together. For example, a very **tactile** family may appear suspicious to others, but this is simply how they show affection. We only know what we are used to, and while the behaviour of others may appear different, it may be an indicator of a happy, well-adjusted family.

tactile
to do with the sense of touch, communicating using touch

A family may deny an individual material items such as toys or clothes, but this again cannot always be viewed as neglect. It may simply be that finances are limited but they give what they can. Another individual may have plenty of clothes, toys or resources but be deprived of affection or family time. Class may dictate that individuals are united as a family but affection is limited and a more formal approach adopted.

Education can also impact heavily on how individuals view risks or incidents of abuse. Knowledge of what to look for is vital and makes sure people are as safe as they can be. Education and learning can also give confidence, allowing individuals to challenge any behaviour or actions that they may think are a risk.

Is there anything you don't like doing or get anxious about as a result of something that happened to you in the past? How do you overcome this fear or anxiety?

An individual who has bad memories of unsafe or abusive incidents may be wary. They may be unwilling to go out after dark, or have a specific fear of being alone, or in groups.

Activity 20

Hassan is 36 years old and has a learning disability. He likes to go out, but his communication is very limited, and he needs support making journeys and carrying out simple tasks. Hassan receives support from his key workers, but they only work part-time, so they are not able to accompany Hassan on many outings and cannot support him to look for a part-time job.

1. Do you think Hassan's needs are being met?
2. Explain your response.
3. What choices should Hassan be able to make for himself?

From the Internet or local press, find an incident where abuse or harm has been carried out. How did you feel when you read this? How do you think the victim's family or friends would feel? How would your feelings and views be different if this had happened to your friend or a member of your family?

Family and friends

Many people have experienced someone close to them being abused or harmed in some way. When something is so difficult to think about, it is only natural to find ways of denying it to ourselves. Sometimes the abuser is a friend or a family member. When this happens it is especially painful for other family members to face and even harder for the individual to tell someone. Sometimes a person outside the immediate family may have a clearer view of what is going on than those more closely involved.

Family and friends may often believe their actions are the correct ones, but they may be restrictive and prevent an individual from developing or learning further. On the other hand, it may be that the individual's actions or wishes restrict the family, for example they may wish to follow the route of crime or addiction, putting their friends or family at risk.

Social care workers

In 2002 the Care Councils produced codes of practice for employers and employees. There is a code for all care workers, as set out by the General Social Care Council. It states that care workers must:

- Protect the rights and promote the interests of individuals and carers.
- Strive to establish and maintain the trust and confidence of individuals and carers.
- Promote the independence of individuals while protecting them from danger or harm.
- Respect the rights of individuals while seeking to ensure that their behaviour does not harm themselves or other people.
- Uphold public trust and confidence in social care services.
- Be accountable for their practice and take responsibility for maintaining and improving their knowledge and skills.

An important part of a carer's job role is making sure that individuals are able to make choices and take control over as much of their lives as possible – this is called empowerment.

Many people who receive care services are often not able to make choices about what happens in their lives. This might be due to many factors, for example their physical ability, where they live, who provides care and the way services are provided, but individuals who are unable to make choices may suffer from low self-esteem and lose confidence in their own abilities.

Deciding if abuse has been carried out is not always easy, as we have differing views on risk and acceptable behaviour, but any doubts must be passed on to the manager for further action. Views on whether abuse has been carried out may depend on previous knowledge and having the experience and the confidence to report such findings. If you, as a carer, have reported an incident before but were ignored, you will be less keen to report anything in the future. Or an incident may have involved the threat or risk of abuse to yourself from an individual in your care and you may not think you will be believed. Whatever the circumstances, it is important to report concerns or observations.

In your role as a care worker, think about how you might feel if you were faced with a disclosure or incident of abuse. What would you do, and who would you tell?

Activity 21

Complete the advert below, identifying the skills you think are needed to be a care assistant.

WANTED: Care Assistant to carry out general duties. You must have previously worked with older people, and should have an up-to-date Certificate in Manual Handling and experience in the use of hoists. The shifts are available on an on-going basis, allowing you to build up working relationships with your clients and for service users to have continuity of support. Pay rates are negotiable, circa £8.00 per hour.

Skills required include:

1. excellent communication
2. ....
3. ....
4. ....
5. ....

Manager of service

It is the responsibility of the manager of the service to ensure that there is a system of appraisal and supervision for staff with the right processes and documentation in place. This supports a programme of staff training to ensure that issues around abuse, reducing risks and protection are fully discussed and understood. A manager is using their knowledge and experience to ensure the safety of all individuals is maintained at all times. Managers have often dealt with allegations, so they will know the process to follow and what might be a risk, or when actual abuse has been carried out.

It is important that a manager considers all aspects when making decisions about potential abuse. As previously mentioned, what may seem abusive to one person may be perfectly acceptable to another. For example, not helping an older person to do their shopping may be neglectful, but it may be for very supportive reasons such as promoting their independence or encouraging mobility. Things may not always be what they seem – check them out further! A manager will have their own views, perceptions and norms on what they see as acceptable practice, and this will help to inform their views of what has been carried out.

Complaint and adult-protection policies must be in place; and the complaint log is developed to maintain a complete record of outcomes and actions taken by the organisation.

Ask to see a copy of the complaints procedure in your setting. How does it relate to your job role? Is it clear and easy to follow?

Other professionals

The Police and social services have joint working arrangements for responding to suspected abuse. Police and social services teams are experienced in this work and will deal sensitively with the individuals and their family or carers. It is important to remember that abuse is a crime and abusers may need to go to court before the abuse stops and they and the abused person get the help they need. The Police may be responsible either for protecting an individual from further abuse or the repercussions of a disclosure or incident, or for charging a suspected abuser in relation to an incident.

There are also support agencies that can help and advise both the abusers and the abused, for example Victim Support, Public Concern at Work and Age Concern. These organisations use their past knowledge, experience and skills to advise and support others. Organisations also take into account other information relating to risk and abuse and may consult with other people responsible for caring for the individual concerned. This of course will all be done with the individual's permission. Partner organisations must work together to ensure that effective communication, reporting and safeguarding take place. Regular reviews and meetings contribute to this and build on established relations.

Family relationships and care provision may be two key areas that need further exploration in case there are aspects that are risks or could be seen as abuse. For example, there may be a history of abuse, the family or carers may not have sufficient income or resources, so care may not be meeting the

Help being given to a person with a disability

It can be a good idea to reflect on an incident and the practice that was carried out during and after it, which may have impacted on the individuals concerned. Have you ever looked back on something you did? Was this helpful?

needs of the individual, but help may be given by other professionals or organisations to ensure that the needs of all parties are met. Joint working can support the identification of potential harm or abuse, as it counters any preconceived ideas any one person may have, and allows for professional judgement to be exercised.

The care organisation

As a result of an incident a care setting may have had to introduce new regulations or procedures, so past experience has had a direct impact. Inspections will require all standards to be met or development plans to be in place so that the organisation can show how they will improve the service they provide.

On the other hand, it may be that there has never been an incident so the setting may be casual and laid back in its monitoring and implementation of procedures. This also needs to be addressed, as incidents can occur at any time and without warning. Every individual will have different views, needs and memories and life experiences to draw on and this will impact on how they wish their care needs to be met. For example they may be vegetarian, or they may never have shared a room or accommodation with anyone. It is important for providers of care to consider these aspects to ensure that care delivery is personal and not delivered to a group as a whole.

The Social Care Inspectorate

The Care Standards Act 2000 established the National Care Standards Commission, now called the Commission for Social Care Inspection (CSCI), which is England's independent regulator for private, voluntary and statutory social care and health care services. As the Commission develops it also reviews its approach to the identification of risk and harm and protection of vulnerable individuals, using past cases to develop policy and practice.

Inspectorates have a responsibility to oversee the quality and safety of all care provision. Care planning and review forms part of this provision and it is important that inspectors encourage and support care settings to explore further what has had an impact on individuals and how this can influence beliefs and preferences. This in turn can raise awareness within inspectorates about how individuals choose to live. Actions that may seem brutal or cruel may in fact be acts of kindness, or may be due to lack of education or understanding.

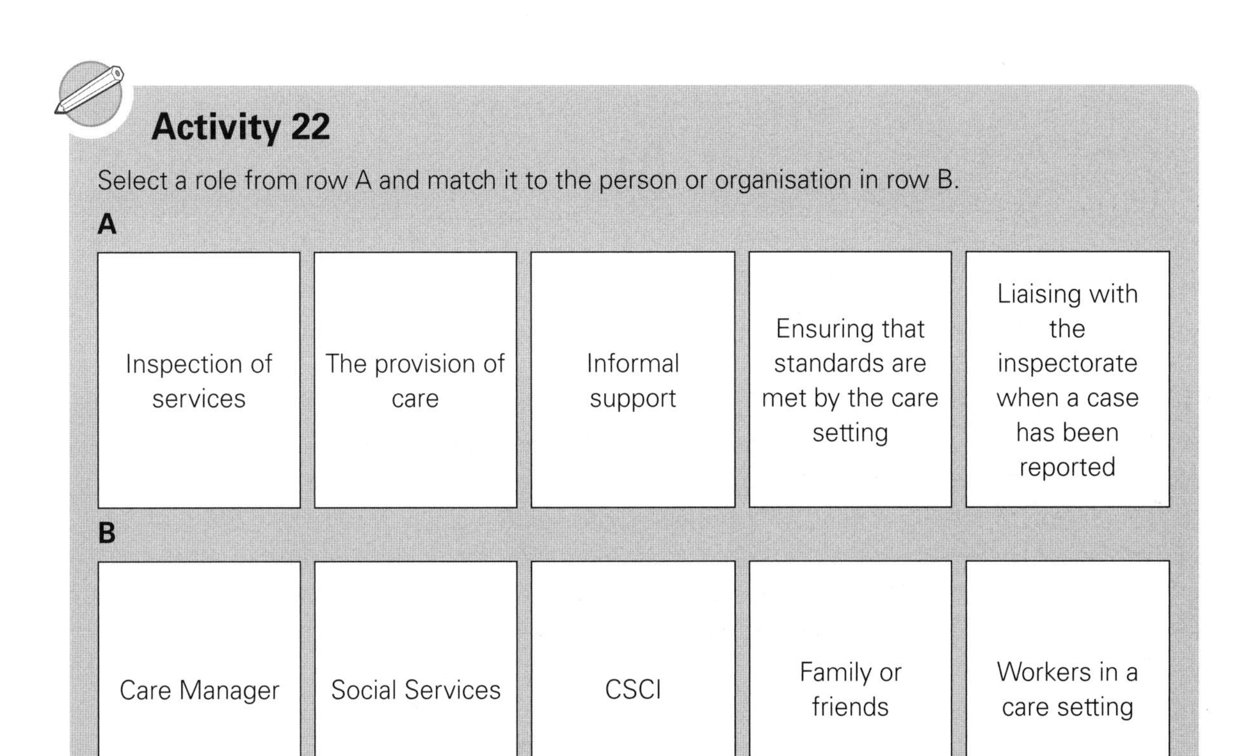

Activity 22

Select a role from row A and match it to the person or organisation in row B.

A

Inspection of services	The provision of care	Informal support	Ensuring that standards are met by the care setting	Liaising with the inspectorate when a case has been reported

B

Care Manager	Social Services	CSCI	Family or friends	Workers in a care setting

3.3 Understand that regardless of perceptions an objective and professional response is required in situations of potential and actual danger, harm and abuse

Abusers often tell their victims that bad things will happen if they tell others about the maltreatment and that it is a secret that must not be shared. Whether the abuser directly threatens the individual or just implies that there will be consequences, the impact is much the same. This fear of what might happen makes disclosure that much more difficult for the individual concerned. How you and others respond to the disclosure or attempts at disclosure is very important. Not responding may leave the individual feeling abandoned or unprotected. On the other hand, being over-emotional or intrusive may scare them and hinder the disclosure. If you as a worker have witnessed an incident you need to report, following the correct procedures is equally important here. If you rush around telling everyone, then confidentiality and trust are breached, so following the correct procedures is vital. So what happens next, and who does what?

What you need to learn

The roles of:

- the social care worker
- the manager of service
- the care organisation
- other professionals
- the commissioning authority
- the Social Care Inspectorate.

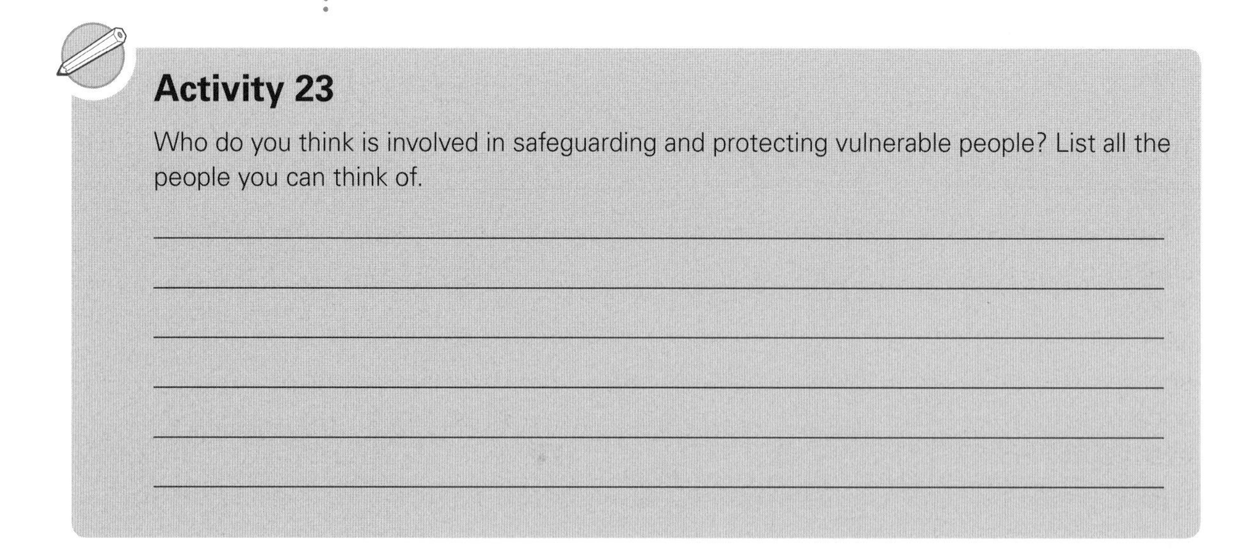

Activity 23

Who do you think is involved in safeguarding and protecting vulnerable people? List all the people you can think of.

The social care worker

In addition to reporting concerns to their manager or senior, all staff should be made aware that they can approach the regulatory bodies, social services or the Police independently to discuss any worries they have about the risk of abuse or incidents they may have witnessed. They should do so if:

- they have concerns that their manager may be involved
- they have grounds for thinking that the manager will not take the matter seriously or act appropriately to protect individuals
- they fear intimidation or have immediate concerns for their own or for an individual's safety.

To start the safeguarding procedures, the member of staff takes action to ensure the immediate safety of anyone at risk and makes contact with their line manager or senior, who then decides whether to make a referral to the multi-agency procedures. This will often be the case, as usually more than one organisation is needed to review and resolve the issue fully.

This referral is made to a an identified safeguarding manager within the setting, who may or may not be the registered care manager. It is their task to co-ordinate all the agencies that need to be involved in the assessment of the risk of abuse or neglect and in making a protection plan for any individual at risk. They often do this by holding meetings with all relevant people present, but may also make a series of telephone calls to the relevant people. The safeguarding manager is also responsible for ensuring that an appropriate professional is designated to review the protection plan and to ensure that any necessary changes are made.

Are there guidelines for you to follow in your work setting?

The safeguarding manager has responsibility for liaising between organisations to ensure that the correct process is carried out, key information is gathered and relevant procedures are followed. These include Local Adult Protection procedures and confidentiality procedures.

Anyone can and should report any concern of suspected or actual abuse or neglect. It is an expectated of all workers and volunteers in agencies that they will make such reports where appropriate. Most workers, for example care workers, nurses, doctors, and social workers, are also expected to do so under their professional code of conduct and under relevant legislation or guidance, for example the Care Standards Act (2000).

It is also important for staff to reinforce that it is not the fault of the individual who has been abused, and support must be given to them. In addition, the person who has witnessed the incident or been told of the disclosure must not investigate the incident themselves, but must pass their concerns on.

In serious cases, evidence may be used as part of an investigation, for example a case conference. It is vital, therefore, to record the information accurately and factually, avoiding personal opinion as this may be difficult to rely on in any future proceeding or investigation.

If an individual talks about possible abuse, the member of staff should:

1. Try to react calmly.
2. Tell the individual that they are right to tell and are not to blame.
3. Listen carefully and take what the individual says seriously.
4. Encourage the individual to talk but do not pressurise them.
5. Reassure the individual. Do not promise confidentiality, but do explain that you will have to speak to someone else who can help.
6. Remember that young or disabled individuals may not be able to express themselves verbally. It may be hard for them to complain or be understood.

Any information a worker has, whether it is simply concerns or hard evidence, must be carefully recorded.

Verbal information can easily change when it is passed on, so a written record is vital. Sometimes this information may need to be included in an individual's care plan to ensure that monitoring is carried out if necessary. You may have a specific form for recording details, but if not it is important that the following are included:

- everything you were told or observed
- any previous concerns you may have had
- what has raised your concerns.

A carer listening to an individual

The manager of service

Care plans and reviews ensure that the needs of individuals are met as far as possible. Regulated services are required to report concerns about the welfare of a vulnerable adult to the Commission for Social Care Inspection (CSCI) within 24 hours of the incident. For example, the Care Homes Regulations 2001 require the registered person to inform the commission without delay of:

- the death of any service user
- the outbreak in the care home of any infectious disease
- any serious injury to a service user
- serious illness of a service user at a care home at which nursing care is not provided
- any event in the care home that adversely affects the well-being or safety of any service user
- any theft, burglary or accident in the care home
- any allegation of misconduct by the registered person or any person who works at the care home.

This report should be made by fax transmission to CSCI within 24 hours of the incident.

It is also the role of the manager to offer support and guidance to the individual concerned and members of staff involved in the incident in any way.

The care organisation

Protecting and safeguarding individuals from harm and abuse needs a coordinated approach, but a major role is played by the organisations that directly provide care. All relevant professionals must be aware of their role in protection and of the knowledge and skills they bring to the setting's prevention and protection efforts. They must also understand the roles, responsibilities, and expertise of other professionals.

Care organisations and providers must follow set procedures. Practice is also informed through organisational procedure (i.e. complaints procedures, reporting incidents, monitoring care plans, health and safety procedures) and the inspections. Through these they are able to monitor and safeguard individuals who have been or may be at risk of abuse.

The organisation, generally through the manager, must ensure that there is no misuse of power and that individuals are treated fairly and equally. Where individuals are unable to exercise their rights, staff must advocate on their behalf. Not to do this would not only be a misuse of power but an infringement of the individual's rights, and would be seen as abuse.

Organisations will work in partnership with other agencies (the Police, CSCI, and social services), working to multi-agency procedures for the protection of vulnerable adults, which clearly outline the procedures and processes following an allegation of abuse or identification of suspected abuse.

Activity 24

Read this extract from a home's inspection report, then answer the questions.

When I walked into the lounge, a female care assistant and a male colleague had been struggling to pick up a female resident. It seemed that she had fallen while they had been moving her from her chair. Rosie (not her real name), who suffers from dementia, was quietly talking to herself. The amazing thing about the scene I had just witnessed was that only hours earlier I had been told that manually moving residents in this way was straightforward 'abuse'.

The home's manager told me that moving and handling training, which was a two-hour talk followed by a verbal test, taught staff that lifting residents under the arm was a drag lift and commonly used.

Drag lifts are a condemned practice and this is a very serious issue. 'Using that lift could fracture someone's shoulder or pull their arm out of its socket,' a care assistant explained. There was also the risk of dropping someone. Over the next three days I lost count of the number of times I saw care assistants using drag lifts. It was one of several areas of concern I was to witness during my visits.

1. What are the main issues here?

____

2. Is abuse being carried out?

____

3. Why might this be?

____

4. What can be done about this?

____

Other professionals

All staff in all agencies should be authorised to call the Police or ambulance service without referring to a senior manager if this would cause delay, in situations where there is immediate risk of harm or need for treatment following an incident. If this does not happen there might later be issues of negligence and it would be viewed as a failure of their duty of care.

In emergencies and when serious crimes have been committed, it may be necessary to contact the Police before contacting social services. What constitutes an emergency should be decided by the manager of any organisation making the referral, but would include any delay that might result in significant harm or loss of evidence.

Referrals to the Police should have the agreement of the victim unless they are not able to make this decision.

The commissioning authority

Everyone has a role to play in the protection of vulnerable people, but the opportunities for appropriate help are greater when agencies work together and have a joint commitment and shared procedures in tackling abuse. It is important that individuals and agencies share information about issues of concern so that a proper assessment of the level of risk is made and action can be taken to prevent further harm. One procedure is the implementation of the Protection of Vulnerable Adults Scheme from July 2004, ensuring the provision of a list of staff who are unsuitable to work with adults in settings regulated by the CSCI; another is the setting up of Adult Protection Committees.

Joint working arrangements to protect vulnerable adults operate in many areas and the Adult Protection Committee is a formal partnership between local health, social care, CSCI and criminal justice agencies. Each agency will select a lead officer for adult protection to ensure effective coordination of services. The Committee also consults with other statutory, independent and voluntary agencies. It is committed to consulting with members of the public, vulnerable adults and their families to make sure that lessons are learned.

The Social Care Inspectorate

The Government created the independent CSCI to achieve greater consistency of regulation and to provide better protection from mistreatment and abuse for vulnerable adults. The commission's duties include registration, inspection and enforcement in relation to services providing personal and nursing care. In addition to their general duty to encourage the improvement of services, CSCI is required to notify the Secretary of State about the availability of provision and quality of services through Part 2 of the Care Standards Act 2000. It has also been recognised that this duty extends to sharing information about problems with service providers to the relevant local authority and to procedures for safeguarding adults.

4 Legislation and guidance

4.1 Understand the legislation, regulations and guidance that govern safeguarding of vulnerable adults from danger, harm and abuse

Most of the roles and tasks in care work are governed by legislation, but the only group where legislation specifically provides for protection from abuse is children. Older people and people with learning disabilities, physical disabilities or mental-health problems have service provisions, rights and many other requirements laid down in law, but no overall legal framework to provide protection from abuse. In this section you will learn about some of this legislation and the impact it has on individuals receiving care.

What you need to learn

- Key legislation.

Key legislation

Health and Safety at Work Act 1974

The Health and Safety at Work Act 1974 lays down the duties of employers and employees and is policed by the Health and Safety Executive (HSE) on behalf of the Health and Safety Commission (HSC).

Under this Act the employer has to protect the health, safety and security of staff, individuals and visitors by:

- drawing up, reviewing and updating safety policy and procedures and ensuring they are carried out
- providing a safe working environment
- providing safe access to and from the workplace
- providing information on health and safety
- providing health and safety training
- carrying out a risk assessment of potential hazards.

In turn, your role as an employee means you are responsible for:

- taking reasonable care of your own health and safety as well as the health and safety of others, for example individuals and their visitors
- co-operating with your employer on health and safety issues
- ensuring that any health and safety equipment is not intentionally damaged.

It is also your added responsibility as a care worker to identify, and then deal with, any potential hazards so that any potential risk to staff, individuals or visitors can be minimised.

Health and safety is a shared responsibility between employer and employee. Both are responsible for the health, safety and welfare of individuals, contractors and visitors, and for ensuring that hazards in the workplace are minimised. Each workplace must have a written health and safety policy, which includes:

- a statement of intent to provide a safe working environment
- the named person responsible for implementing the policy
- the names of individuals responsible for any particular health and safety hazards
- a list of potential health and safety hazards and the procedures to be followed when working with these
- a procedure for recording accidents and illnesses at work.

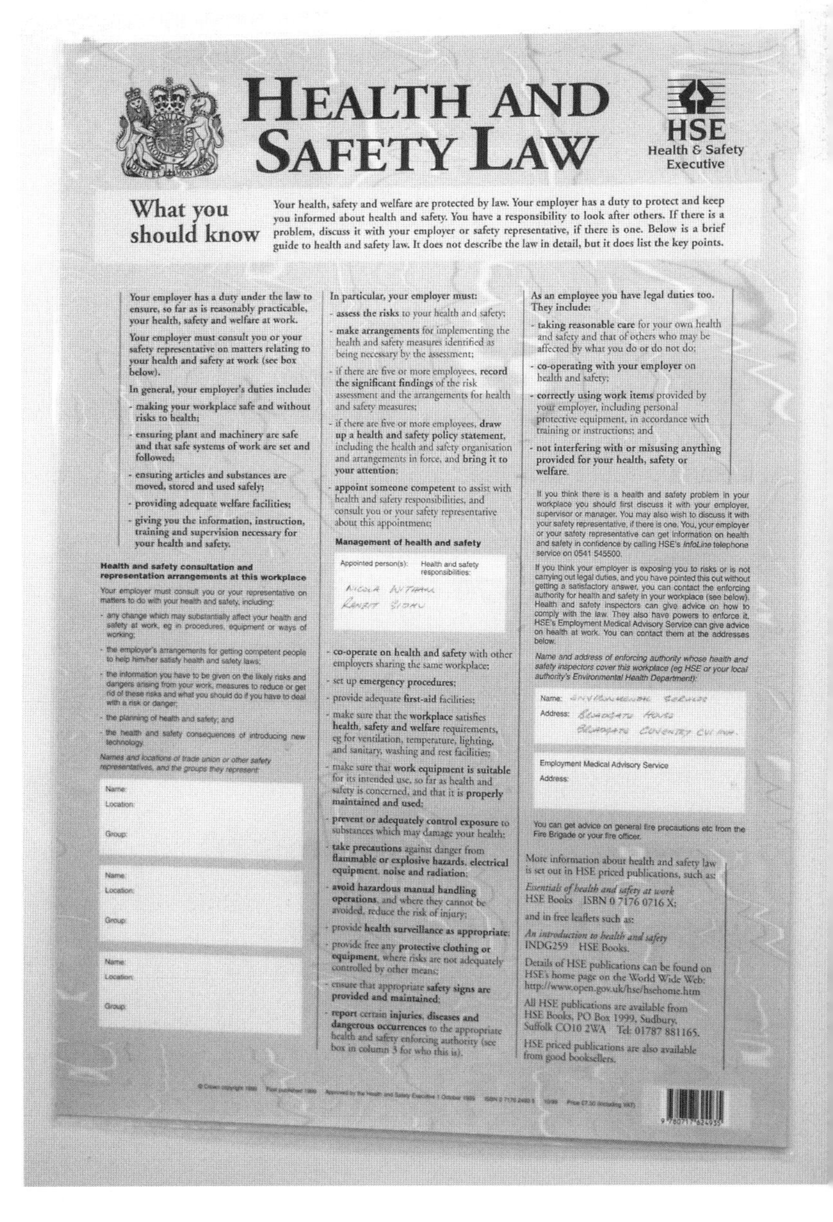

The law

Management of Health and Safety at Work Regulations 1999

These Regulations were originally introduced in 1993 in response to a European Community Directive. The original Management of Health and Safety at Work Regulations 1992 have been amended several times:

- Management of Health and Safety at Work (Amendment) Regulations 1994

- Health and Safety (Young Persons) Regulations 1997
- Fire Precautions (Workplace) Regulations 1997.

Because the Regulations had changed so much, they were amended again in 1999 and the HSE revised its Approved Code of Practice (ACoP). The Regulations serve to support the requirements of the Health and Safety at Work Act and aim to identify an employer's common law duty of care and clarify the employer's responsibility to identify health and safety problems and to take action to correct them. The Management of Health and Safety at Work Regulations 1999 require employers to carry out risk assessments, make arrangements to implement necessary measures, appoint competent people and arrange for appropriate information and training.

Activity 23

Complete the table below: identify the hazards that could be within the area, then suggest how they could be avoided.

Area	Hazard	Ways to avoid the hazard
Stairs/steps		
Floors		
Roads		
Kitchen areas		
Entrances/exits		
Transport		
Fire doors		

Human Rights Act 1998

This is an important piece of legislation that affects large areas of our lives – you may have read about it in newspapers, or heard about it on television or the radio. The Human Rights Act doesn't spell out things you must or mustn't do, but is more like a series of principles, called articles or protocols. If an individual wanted to take someone to court under the Human Rights Act, they would have to show that one of these principles has been broken.

However, the Human Rights Act does not apply to all care provision. Private and voluntary sector provision is not covered, but there are plans to extend the protection of human-rights law to all people in residential care. This will not immediately stop abuse or provide an overnight change in culture, but will be a huge step forward for individuals living in care homes.

The Human Rights Act also says that public authorities must respect people's rights under the Act. Public authorities include government departments, the Police and local councils.

The Act includes an individual's right to:

- freedom from torture and inhuman or degrading treatment
- liberty and security of persons
- respect for private and family life, home and correspondence
- freedom of thought, conscience and religion
- freedom of expression
- freedom of assembly and association
- peaceful enjoyment of possessions and protection of property.

Care Standards Act 2000

The purpose of the Care Standards Act 2000 is to make sure that the care of vulnerable people in different types of care settings is properly regulated by improving care standards and introducing consistency in the regulation of the services provided. Previously this range of care services was regulated under the Registered Homes Act 1984. The 1984 Act was passed to protect the welfare of vulnerable adults in residential care in the private sector, but is now seen as outdated.

The Act introduced the following changes:

- For the first time, local authorities now have to be regulated and meet the same care standards as the independent sector providers.
- The Act introduced a new, independent regulatory body for social care known as the National Care Standards Commission. In 2002 the NCSC was replaced by the Commission for Social Care Inspection (CSCI). The CSCI monitors care homes on a national basis and they are no longer regulated by local inspectorate units.
- The Government introduced national minimum care standards for care providers.

Find out what the following organisations do and how this might impact on your role as a care worker.

- GSCC
- CSCI
- Skills for Care
- Social Care Institute for Excellence (SCIE).

- The Act established the General Social Care Council for England and the Care Council for Wales. The councils register social care workers, regulate the training of social workers and raise standards in social care through codes of conduct and practice.
- Domiciliary care agencies are required to register and any organisation providing services for people in their own homes must be registered.

Protection of Vulnerable Adults (POVA)

The Care Standards Act 2000 included provision for a Protection of Vulnerable Adults (POVA) register to be kept of all those people considered unsuitable to work with vulnerable adults. Care organisations can contribute to this register by reporting any proven cases of abuse, and by referring to the register whenever recruiting new staff. The introduction of the scheme in July 2004 has given a stronger basis to protection work. It provides a register of care workers in regulated care settings who have harmed or placed a vulnerable adult at risk of harm. The register is held by the Department of Education and Skills on behalf of the Secretary of State and is held alongside the Protection of Children Act Scheme.

Safeguarding of Vulnerable Adults Scheme 2004 (based on Care Standards Act 2000)

In 2003 Ian Huntley was convicted of the murders of Holly Wells and Jessica Chapman. The trial showed up major flaws in the police checking system. Huntley had undergone full police checks before being appointed as school caretaker, yet these did not show up a series of allegations of sexual offences committed between 1995 and 1999. The Birchard Inquiry was set up by the Home Secretary and its findings highlighted the importance of an in-depth recruitment process in order to keep children and vulnerable adults safe. Effective recruitment and vetting must pay attention to all of the pre-employment checks including written references, identity and qualifications checks and full employment history, as well as the checks undertaken by the **Criminal Records Bureau (CRB)**. As a result the Government has developed a new vetting scheme in response to the recommendations made in the Birchard report, and this is now set out in the Safeguarding Vulnerable Groups Act 2006. The scheme will enable the employer to be directly informed of any change in an employee's barred status.

Criminal Records Bureau (CRB)
an organisation that provides wider access to criminal record information through the disclosure service. This service enables organisations in the public, private and voluntary sectors to make safer recruitment decisions by identifying candidates who may be unsuitable for certain work, especially those that involve children or vulnerable adults. The CRB was established under Part V of the Police Act 1997 and was launched in March 2002

'No Secrets' – DH guidance

In 2000 the Department of Health and the Home Office published the document 'No Secrets': guidance on developing and implementing multi-agency policy and procedures to protect vulnerable adults from abuse. In 2005, the document

No secrets

'Safeguarding Adults' was published by the Department of Health in partnership with the Commission for Social Care Inspection to provide a national framework of standards for good practice and outcomes in adult-protection work. The publication's intention was to provide a toolkit for organisations providing health and care services for adults so they could develop an evidence-based good practice framework to ensure the safety of vulnerable adults. In addition, the guidance states that other statutory agencies should 'work together in partnership to ensure that appropriate policies, procedures and practices are in place and implemented locally.'

Adult protection protocols are intended to lead workers through the process of reporting protection concerns; sharing information during the evaluation of initial reports, the planning, investigation, assessment and decision-making phases and then contributing as necessary to a case conference during which the issues of on-going protection, support and action will be explored.

Health Act 1999

The Health Act 1999 came into force in April 2000 and included the latest attempt to get rid of the division between the health services (funded and provided by the NHS) and the social services (run by local councils). The distinction between health and social care is often unclear to individuals using the services, who often complain of being pushed from one to the other when trying to sort out different parts of their care package. There is confusion over who does what: if a client is given a bath, is it a health care bath or a social care bath? Issues of this kind can lead to a lack of quality of care and funding issues. Another problem is when NHS beds are 'blocked' by people who no longer require hospital care but whose social care packages have yet to be arranged because of funding problems. Councils and health providers are being encouraged to work in partnership and make better use of resources so that they can provide the care that is required.

NHS and Community Care Act 1990

The NHS and Community Care Act 1990 helps people live safely in the community. Social services assess the needs of individuals and arrange for the provision of social care services to meet these needs. Other responsibilities include: procedures for receiving comments and complaints, registration and inspection requirements and a review of the individual's ability to contribute.

Mental Health Act 1983

The Mental Health Act 1983 is an Act of the Parliament of the United Kingdom but applies only to England and Wales. The Act covers the reception, care and initial and on-going treatment of mentally disordered people, the supervision of their property and other matters relating to their care. Specifically the Act provides the legislation by which people suffering from a mental disorder can be detained in hospital and have their disorder assessed or treated against their wishes, often known as 'sectioning'. The Act's implementation is reviewed and regulated by a special health authority known as the Mental Health Act Commission (MHAC).

Mental Capacity Act 2005

This Act was fully implemented in 2007 and and replaced Part 7 of the Mental Health Act 1983. One of its key features is the criminalisation of neglect. The Act is underpinned by five key priniciples:

1. An individual is assumed to be capable unless proven otherwise.
2. An individual should be supported to make their own decisions.
3. An individual has the right to make unorthodox decisions.
4. The individual's best interests must be the focus.
5. Any intervention should be as unresttrictive as possible.

The Mental Capacity Act will help people make their own decisions and will protect individuals who cannot make decisions about some things (known as 'lacking capacity'). In addition the Act tells people what to do to help someone make their own decisions, how to work out if someone can make their own decisions and what to do if someone can make decisions about some things but not about other things. For example they may be able to make decisions about their care but require assistance in sorting out their finances.

The Act also introduces rules relating to care and treatment. For example, if an individual needs care or treatment, someone can give them the care or treatment they need, but the person providing these must follow the best-interests checklist to decide what is in the individual's best interest. Sometimes it is necessary for a doctor to give treatment to an individual who does not have the mental capacity to say whether they want it or not.

An advance decision is when someone who has mental capacity decides that they do not want a particular type of treatment if they lack capacity in the future; a doctor must respect this decision. In addition, an advance decision must be about the treatment an individual wants to refuse and when they want to refuse it. If the advance decision says no to treatment that may keep them alive, it must say this clearly and be signed by the individual. Another person may sign an advance decision on the individual's behalf, but only if the individual agrees and can see them sign it.

Data Protection Act 1998

The Data Protection Act 1998 (DPA) governs the storage and processing of personal data held in manual records and on computers. The Act protects the individual's rights by forcing organisations to follow sound and proper practices, known as the Data Protection Principles (DPP). This covers all manual or computerised individual or employee records held by residential or nursing care homes.

According to the DPA there are main principles under which personal data should be kept and collected. Personal data should:

- be obtained fairly and lawfully
- be held for specified and lawful purposes
- be processed in accordance with the person's rights under the DPA
- be adequate, relevant and not excessive in relation to that purpose
- be kept accurate and up to date
- not be kept for longer than is necessary for its given purpose
- be subject to appropriate safeguards against unauthorised use, loss or damage.

One of the most important aspects of the DPA is that personal data may be processed only if the individual has given their consent. All files kept about residents or staff should be confidential and individuals should know what records are being kept about them and why they are being kept.

Individuals should be given access to what is said about them in any personal records maintained by the home, and information should be withheld only in exceptional circumstances. All data, particularly sensitive or confidential data, must be stored securely. Manual records such as personnel files and resident care files should be kept in locked filing cabinets, preferably within an office that is locked when unattended. Care must be taken when working on confidential files that they are put away securely and not left out on a desk where people could walk by and see them. Where data is stored electronically on a computer the following steps should be considered:

- Check regularly on the accuracy of data being entered (remember that a home may be liable for inaccurate or erroneous data).
- Ensure that the computer system is secure by checking that it has a backup system, that lost data can be recovered and that backups are stored in a safe and secure place.
- Ensure that all staff who need to use the computer system are thoroughly trained in its use.
- Ensure that passwords are used for access to different parts of the system, and that these are regularly changed and not passed on to people who should not have them.
- Use screen blanking to ensure that personal data is not visible when not in use by authorised staff.
- Review the positioning of terminals to ensure that unauthorised staff or individuals cannot casually view personal data on screen.
- Ensure that confidential or private printouts are stored securely and safely and that they are collected immediately if printed onto a networked printer.

Disability Discrimination Act 1995 amended 2005

The Disability Discrimination Act 1995 (DDA 1995) is a UK parliamentary Act of 1995, which makes it unlawful to discriminate against people in respect of their disabilities in relation to the jobs they can do, the provision of goods and services, education and transport. The Government set up the Disability Rights Commission (DRC) to provide support during the implementation of the Act. Equivalent legislation exists in Northern Ireland, which is enforced by the Northern Ireland Equality Commission.

It is still allowable for employers to have reasonable medical criteria for employment, and to expect adequate performance from all employees once any reasonable adjustments have been made.

In addition to making requirements on employers, the DDA 1995 requires service providers, for example shops and businesses, to make 'reasonable adjustments' when providing access to goods, facilities, services or premises. A 'reasonable adjustment' may be the use of a ramp to gain access to the building, or installing a loop system for those with a hearing impairment.

The Disability Discrimination Act (DDA) 1995, as amended, does not allow discrimination against disabled people in a range of circumstances, including in employment and occupation, education, transport, and the provision of goods, facilities and services.

The DDA 2005 completed the implementation of the Disability Rights Task Force recommendations, and included the extension of the DDA 1995 to cover public transport, and the introduction of the requirement for public authorities to promote equality for disabled people.

Care scenario: Mrs Morgan

Mrs Morgan is 80 years of age, has a visual impairment and is in constant pain from an arthritic hip. She requires a hip replacement and has been on the waiting list of Mr Smyth, the consultant, for over two years. When she sees Mr Smyth he is always dismissive of her and does not try to communicate with her to meet her needs.

Mrs Morgan attends a luncheon club once a week, where she meets her friend Mrs Davies, who is 62. During their conversation, Mrs Davies states that she is going into hospital on the following Wednesday to have a hip replacement. Mrs Morgan asks her how long she has been on the waiting list. Mrs Davies says that she first saw Mr Smyth three months ago.

Arriving back at the home that afternoon, Mrs Morgan telephones Mr Smyth's secretary and asks how far up the waiting list she is. Mr Smyth's secretary tells her that it will be at least another year before she is considered. Mrs Morgan asks why her friend has been given a date much sooner that her although she has only been on the waiting list for three months. Mr Smyth's secretary states that she cannot discuss other patients with Mrs Morgan and bids her goodbye.

When you call into Mrs Morgan's bedroom to assist her to bed she seems very distressed when she relates this experience to you.

1. What legislation is being breached in this incident?
2. What should have happened?

National Service Framework for Older People

In 2001 the Government produced a National Service Framework for Older People (NSF), which set out the standards of care required for people over the age of 55. The framework is a ten-year programme requiring health-care providers and local authorities to develop new ways of working and of providing services. The milestones and targets for the implementation of the NSF for older people include:

- the introduction of a single assessment process for health and social care for older people by April 2004
- the requirement for primary care trusts to make sure that all general practices are using a protocol agreed in liaison with health and social services on how to diagnose, treat and care for patients with dementia by April 2004
- health improvement plans and other relevant plans, developed with local authority and independent sector providers, should have included in them the development of an integrated mental health service by April 2004.

Care scenario: Maria

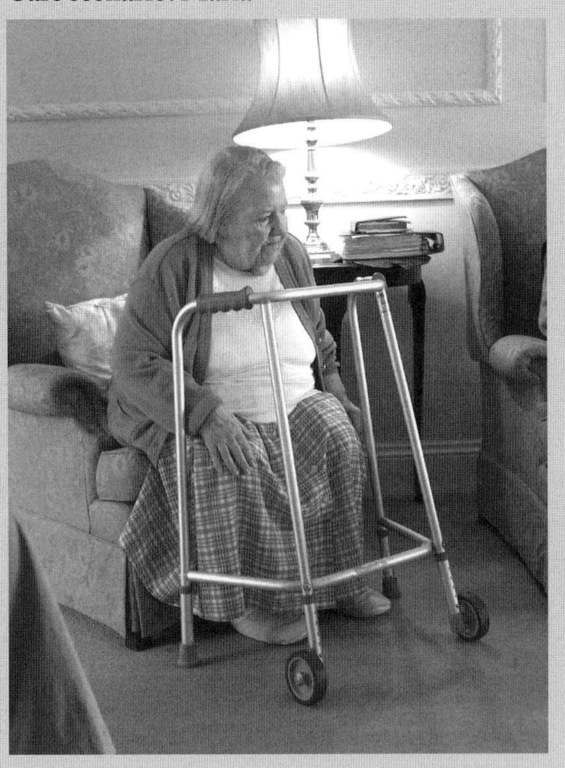

Maria is 71 years old and has Parkinson's disease. As a result her mobility is limited and she cannot be left alone as she falls frequently. Maria is cared for by her husband, who gave up a job he enjoyed to care for her, and has two daughters who visit as often as they can.

Maria is reluctant to go out because she feels people are always looking at her. Maria is very angry about her condition and can be very uncooperative about any help offered.

1. How could the National Service Framework help Maria?
2. What key aspects would it help her with and how could it improve her life choices?

Race Relations Act 1976 and amendments 2000, 2003

The 1976 Act made race discrimination unlawful in relation to employment, education, training and the provision of goods, facilities and services. The Act applies to discrimination in three main groups: direct discrimination, indirect discrimination and victimisation.

Direct discrimination happens when a person treats another person less favourably on the basis of their colour, race, nationality, ethnic or national origin, for example:

- refusing to serve ethnic minority customers
- ignoring obvious racial harassment of employees.

Indirect discrimination is when a condition or requirement is set for a job that automatically rules out a group of applicants due to their origin.

Victimisation is when individuals want to exercise their rights but are stopped from doing so because of their race. This includes people who help others in following up complaints regarding race discrimination.

The Race Relations Amendment Act 2000 came into force on 2 April 2001 and requires public authorities to take the lead in eliminating racial discrimination and promoting equality of opportunity and good relations between individuals of different ethnic groups.

The new public duty requires public bodies to implement race equality in all aspects of employment matters, such as recruitment and selection, training, promotion, discipline and dismissal.

The Race Relations Act 1976 (Amendment) Regulations 2003 includes the EC Article 13 Race Directive. The Regulations update the Race Relations Act by changing the definition of indirect discrimination and revising the way in which the burden of proof applies, as well as removing some of the exceptions from the legislation. These changes bring the Race Relations Act into line with the rest of UK anti-discrimination law to form part of a consistent legislative framework.

Enduring Power of Attorney Act 1985 (obsolete since the introduction of the Mental Capacity Act)

Power of Attorney was a legal document that allowed one person, called the Donor, to give another person, known as the Attorney, permission to act on their behalf and in their name in respect of their financial affairs. Before the Enduring Power of Attorney Act 1985, every Power of Attorney was automatically formally cancelled if the Donor became mentally incapable, but this presented two problems:

1. It was not always obvious when a Donor actually became incapable.
2. It was not possible to privately arrange in advance to give someone authority to handle their affairs when, at a later date, they had become incapable.

The only solution was to apply to the Court of Protection for the appointment of a Receiver, an expensive and complicated process.

By introducing an Enduring Power of Attorney, the Donor appointed an Attorney who, if the Donor then became mentally unable to manage their own affairs, could continue to act as Attorney. The named power had to be registered with the Court of Protection, and once registered, the Attorney could continue to act on behalf of the Donor without further input from the Court. The Power therefore 'endured' or continued beyond mental incapacity.

Freedom of Information Act 2000

The Freedom of information Act (FOI) was passed in November 2000 and came into effect fully from 1 January 2005. It gives people a right of access to information held about them by public bodies. The range of public bodies covered by FOI is very wide, ranging from central government departments to individual schools and parish councils. A full list of the bodies affected – FOI authorities – can be found in Schedule 1 of the Act. There is a separate Act covering public authorities in Scotland – the Freedom of Information (Scotland) Act 2002.

The FOI applies to information, however old it is, and whether it is in the National Archives or is still held by the government department it came from. The 30-year standard closure period no longer decides access to records but instead information is assumed to be 'open' right from the start unless one of the exemptions set out in the Act applies. Exemptions are the grounds for withholding information and they are clearly defined in the Act. The exemptions are limited in number and are usually used where some harm might result if the information were to be released.

Sex Discrimination Act 1975

Sex Discrimination Act 1975 (SDA) protects against discrimination of both men and women. It makes sex discrimination unlawful in employment, vocational training, education, the provision and sale of goods, facilities and services, premises and in the exercise of public functions and duties.

In employment and vocational training it is also against the law to discriminate against someone on the grounds that they are married or a civil partner or on the ground of **gender reassignment**.

gender reassignment
altering primary characteristics of sex and roles

The Sex Discrimination (Gender Reassignment) Regulations 1999 clarify UK law relating to gender reassignment. They provide a baseline in order to prevent discrimination against transsexual people on the grounds of sex in pay and treatment in employment and vocational training. This is as a result of a ruling by the European Court of Justice that the dismissal of an employee undergoing gender reassignment is contrary to the European Equal Treatment Directive. The UK and all Member States are obligated to implement European law. The Gender Recognition Act, 2004, amended parts of the SDA to apply to transgendered people.

On 1 December 2003 the Employment Equality (Sexual Orientation) Regulations 2003 came into force to outlaw discrimination in the employment field based on sexual orientation and to implement the EC Equal Treatment Framework Directive 2000/78/EC.

Public Interest Disclosure Act 1998 ('whistle-blower's charter')

The Public Interest Disclosure Act 1998 (PIDA) created a framework for whistle-blowing across the private, public and voluntary sectors. The Act provides nearly every individual in the workplace with protection from victimisation when they raise concerns about malpractice following the Act's provisions. The protection most readily available under the Act is where a worker who is concerned about malpractice, raises the issue within the organisation or with the person responsible for the malpractice. The intention of this provision is to reassure workers that it is safe and acceptable for them to raise such concerns. Employers are encouraged to establish proper procedures for dealing with disclosures, or whistle-blowing. The Act also sets out the circumstances where the disclosure of the malpractice outside of the organisation is in the public interest and should therefore be protected.

When would you use a whistle-blower's charter? Do you know where to find it in your setting?

Modernising Social Services 1998

The White Paper, *Modernising Social Services* was published in November 1998 and sets out the Government's programme for modernising social services and tackling the perceived failures in terms of:

- protection of vulnerable adults
- coordination of services between different agencies
- flexibility of services to meet users' needs

- clarity over what services are, or should be, provided
- consistency in standards and levels of service across different areas
- inefficiency and variation in costs between councils.

The White Paper proposed the setting up of eight regional Commissions for Care Standards (CCS). It was intended that these would be based on the boundaries of the NHS and Social Care regions and would be independent statutory bodies with their own chair appointed by the Secretary of State and a management board that would include representatives from local authorities and health authorities, together with user and provider representatives.

Sexual Offences Act 2003

The Sexual Offences Act is the first major overhaul of sexual offences legislation for over a century. It sets out a strong and clear approach to this sensitive area of the law.

The new laws put victims first and are designed to protect everyone: adults, children and vulnerable people, from abuse and exploitation. The laws reflect the reality of life today and set out clear boundaries about what is, and is not, acceptable. The laws are non-discriminatory, so that men and women of all sexual orientations are equally protected. They set down strong penalties for sexual crime, and give the courts and Police the clarity they need to do their job and help protect the public from abusers.

In addition to the legislation itself, support for victims of sexual crime is being improved all the time, with better methods of police investigation and increased support services for victims and witnesses.

Domestic Violence, Crime and Victims Act 2004

The Domestic Violence, Crime and Victims Act 2004 introduces new powers for the police and courts to enable them to deal with offenders, while also improving the support and protection that victims receive.

The provisions of this Act include:

- Making it an offence to breach a non-molestation order; with a penalty of up to five years in prison.
- Making common assault an arrestable offence.
- Giving cohabiting same-sex couples the same protection as heterosexual couples and extending the availability of non-molestation orders to couples who have never lived together or been married.
- Giving courts the power to impose a restraining order where the defendant has been acquitted but the court believes an order is necessary to protect the victim.

- Providing a code of practice, binding on all criminal justice agencies, so that all victims receive the support, protection, information and advice they need. If a person fails to comply with the code it does not make them liable to criminal or civil proceedings. However, the code is admissible in criminal or civil proceedings and a court may take into account a failure to comply with the code in determining a question in the proceedings.

The Racial and Religious Hatred Act 2006

The Racial and Religious Hatred Act creates a new offence of intentionally stirring up religious hatred against people on religious grounds, bridging a gap in the current legislation.

Existing offences in the Public Order Act 1986 legislate against inciting racial hatred. Jews and Sikhs have been deemed by the courts to be racial groups and are protected under this legislation, but other groups such as Muslims and Christians are considered to be religious rather than racial groups and have therefore not previously received any protection under the law.

Activity 26

Identify the pieces of legislation that relate to the protection of vulnerable individuals.

Legislation relating to the protection of vulnerable adults – but which ones?				
Equal Opportunities Act	The Misuse of Drugs Act (1971)	The Misuse of Drugs Regulations 2003	National Minimum Standards	The Data Protection Act 1998
The Control of Substances Hazardous to Health	EEC Directives	Local policies and procedures	The Care Standards Act 2000	The Human Rights Act 1998
Road Traffic Act 1999	Health and Safety at Work Act 1974	The Income Tax (Trading and Other Income) Act 2005	Food Premises (Registration) Regulations 1991	The Transmissible Spongiform Encephalopathies (No. 2) Regulations 2006
Public Interest Disclosure Act (1998)	Reporting of Injuries, Diseases and Dangerous Occurrences 1995	The Care Homes Regulations 2001	Children Act 2004	Protection of Vulnerable Adults Scheme (POVA)

4.2 Understand the organisation's policies and procedures with regard to the safeguarding of vulnerable adults from danger, harm and abuse

Policies alone don't solve problems, in fact they can complicate things unless they are clearly written and observed. What a policy does is define the ideal towards which all staff should work. Policies should be clear, comprehensive, and well defined, identifying rules and procedures that regulate practice. Good policy protects not only individual workers and those receiving the service but the organisation as a whole. In this section you will learn about the impact that policies have on you and on the work you carry out.

What you need to learn

- A safe and secure environment.
- Correct recruitment procedures for staff working in social care settings.
- 'No secrets' – including whistle-blowing.
- Policy on visitors.
- Complaints procedure.

A safe and secure environment

If people are to live and work together in a setting, they must do so in a safe and secure environment. A health and safety policy is a plan detailing how an organisation or manager is going to manage health and safety issues. The health and safety policy should set out the organisation's commitment to manage risks and meet legal duties. It should also inform staff of their duties and responsibilities and the steps that they need to take in order to fulfil those duties. An organisation must have a safety policy, and if five or more people are employed it must be written down. The same principles apply, regardless of whether or not the policy is written down.

Safety and security

Correct recruitment procedures for staff working in social care settings

Inspectors are looking for evidence of a thorough and carefully managed recruitment and selection process, with emphasis on appropriate checks and vetting procedures to safeguard all individuals. This includes evidence of CRB checks, references, employment history, medical declaration, qualifications, and the implementation of a robust recruitment and selection process, for each staff member.

Inspectors will review the policies and procedures relating to staffing in the setting, with particular emphasis on verifying the processes for the following key areas.

References and employment history

Thorough and effective referencing of job applicants is one way to screen potential recruits' suitability to work in the setting. It is good practice to take up a minimum of two references that can account for the last two years, on any applicant under consideration. Ex-employer references can offer essential insights into the applicant's working history, but sometimes it's what they don't say that can cause concern.

If references are sought after identifying the successful candidate from interview, a verbal offer of employment subject to satisfactory references can be extended, which enables the employer to revoke the offer if unsatisfactory references or other information come to light.

Think about when you started your job. What checks and procedures did you have to go through?

Character references

In some cases, for example, where the applicant is returning to work, it will not be possible to seek ex-employer references. In such cases, at least two character references must be sought. These must not be obtained from family members or close personal friends, but preferably from people who know the individual in a professional capacity.

Qualifications

Ask all candidates to bring their certificates and personal portfolio with them to interview, and take photocopies of relevant training-related certificates. Once a verbal offer of employment has been extended, you could verify any certificates that you might be unsure about, with the appropriate awarding body.

A recruitment policy should:

- demonstrate an organised approach to planning recruitment

- contain a written policy on the Recruitment and Selection Process, including shortlisting, interview and referencing/ screening procedures
- address advertising – how, when and where?
- include a timescale plan for the recruitment process
- include written policies on Equal Opportunities relating to staff.

Qualifications

'No secrets' – including whistle-blowing

Members of staff may be the first to spot anything that is seriously wrong within the care setting. However, they may not say anything because they think this would be disloyal, or they might be worried that their suspicions are not justified. They may also be worried that they or someone else may be victimised. Members of the public may also have concerns, so it is important to have a whistle-blowing policy to help staff and the public to voice their concerns. If an allegation is true they have nothing to fear, but deciding to blow the whistle is not easy.

The policy should explain that the organisation will keep any concerns confidential if this is what the whistle-blower wants. In this case names will not be revealed without permission unless it is necessary to do so by law.

This policy is intended to deal with serious or sensitive concerns such as the following:

- fraud or corruption
- individuals being mistreated
- any act that is unlawful
- any danger or risk to health and safety
- the environment being damaged, for example, by pollution
- a staff member abusing their position for any unauthorised use or for personal gain
- a staff member deliberately not following a policy, an official code of practice or any law or regulation
- a person failing to meet the required professional standards
- a person being discriminated against because of their race, colour, religion, ethnic or national origin, disability, age, sex, sexuality, class or home life.

A concern raised may be about members of staff, people who work directly for the organisation, suppliers or individuals receiving the service.

Policy on visitors

Many settings have an open-door policy for visitors. They are welcome to visit at any time during the day, often preferably not during mealtimes, and are invited and encouraged to take individuals out for day trips, meals, visits or appointments.

The policy should also state that individuals have the right not to see visitors if they so wish. Visitors are requested to advise the staff of their arrival and departure and to sign the visitors' book. These aspects all contribute to safeguarding individuals from harm or abuse, ensuring that the organisation is aware of who is in the setting and when individuals are out of the building. It is a requirement for fire regulations to have details of who is in the building, including contractors, visitors and volunteers, so a register must be maintained.

When operating a policy of open visiting, it is important to identify and state the most convenient visiting times. These are generally between 11 a.m. and 8 p.m., when there will also be a member of staff available for visitors to speak to if necessary. At other times, staff tend to be busy and their priority must be the individuals they are caring for.

It may also include a statement such as: 'The manager and deputy manager will also be available between 10 a.m. and 5 p.m., and visitors are encouraged to call in at the office for a chat at any time.'

Complaints procedure

It is important to always try to settle any difficulty at a personal level first, either with the person concerned or their manager. The problem may simply be due to a failure of communication or a misunderstanding and if an informal approach fails, there are a number of procedures that can be followed, depending on the circumstances.

As a first step it is often helpful to talk things through with someone who can offer advice about next steps. Your local Citizens Advice Bureau, Alzheimer's Society branch or Age Concern group may be able to help.

Activity 27

Look for a complaints or compliments procedure or policy in your local surgery, shop or restaurant, or anywhere you think might have one.

1. Was it easy to find?
2. Was it easy to follow and understand?
3. Did it give you enough information to be able to compliment or complain if you wanted to?

If they have a complaint about any of the services provided by social services, individuals are advised to contact the social services department, who will provide a copy of their complaints procedure and explain how to use it.

If the complaint involves services provided by the NHS, individuals can use the NHS complaints procedure. This is accessed by asking the particular service for a copy of their complaints procedure or contacting their local health authority or NHS Direct.

If the complaint is about another local authority department, a voluntary organisation or a private agency, the individual must ask them for a copy of their complaints procedure. If the complaint involves home care services, they can also complain to the area CSCI office, which has powers to ensure that agencies providing home care meet certain standards and will follow up all complaints made.

An example of a complaints procedure

Parc Menai Residential Home Complaints procedure

There are three stages:

Stage 1 Informal

Staff and managers involved in providing the service that you are unhappy with are responsible for resolving your complaint. The Care Management team may be able to help with this stage.

Stage 2 Formal

If you are unhappy about the response you received at Stage 1, you can request that your complaint is considered under Stage 2 of the process. This means that an investigation will be undertaken within 28 days, by someone who has no involvement with the service you are complaining about. You will receive a response telling you what action will be taken as a result of the investigation. If there are any delays in this process the Care Management Team will keep you informed.

Stage 3 Review panel

If you are not satisfied with the response you received at Stage 2, you will be advised about the next stage. You can ask the Care Management Team to refer your concerns about the investigation process and/or the response that you received from us to a Review Panel. The Care Management Team will write to you with details of this process.

Additional information

The use of the Complaints Procedure does not affect your rights to use other ways of raising your concerns and complaints, for example through your local councillor, MP or a solicitor.

The Commission for Social Care Inspection is the public body regulating social care, and private and voluntary health care services, throughout England. They can be contacted by telephone at 0845 015 0120, or in writing at Commission for Social Care Inspection, 33 Greycoat Street, London, W1P 2QF.

Trainer notes

These Trainer notes have been written to help you give the best advice and guidance possible to your care workers. A selection of the activities on pages 2–103 are discussed, along with further ways in which you can encourage successful completion of training. The Trainer notes will also give you guidance on what additional texts or information sources you will need to give learners opportunities to achieve the most from this book.

Roles and boundaries

1.1 Understand the role, responsibilities and boundaries of the worker with regard to safeguarding individuals from danger, harm and abuse

This section will guide you through the role of support services in protecting individuals from danger, harm and abuse. It is vital that staff are aware of the limits and boundaries of their job roles but also that they are aware of the roles and responsibilities of others.

Activity 1

Encourage learners to establish the content of policies and the support they can expect.

Care scenario – Sarah, page 7

Sarah would greatly benefit from an advocate or key workers but must be communicated with in a manner suitable to her. Sarah has many care needs, including to be safe and free from harm or risk, to have appropriate medication and to socialise as she wishes.

Activity 2

Encourage learners to think of a range of approaches in meeting needs: to be creative while also considering respect and dignity.

For example, in order to follow a preferred diet it may be that an individual can become involved in the buying and preparation of their meals. This promotes independence and offers additional activities that may not otherwise be available.

Activity 3

This activity is to encourage learners to think beyond asking other carers. It is important to include the individual as much as possible, but also to liaise with family, friends, other carers, other professionals or staff working on activities. Any person coming into contact with an individual can offer an insight into their needs and preferences.

Care scenario – Mrs Mills, page 12

Mrs Mills is at risk as she is getting forgetful and may leave her door unlocked or start to wander. Mrs Mills should be fully assessed and her needs and wishes taken into consideration to ensure they are met as far as possible.

Activity 4

Key to this activity is the contents of the policy. What needs to be carried out should be set out in a sequential manner. For example, the visitor must identify themselves using agreed ID, then sign in and wait in an appointed place. The policy must also include how to raise the alarm, this may be by using an alarm system or by informing the senior in charge.

Activity 5

It is important to encourage learners to learn to look for hazards and to be are of how to do this and what to look for. For example, disposing of clinical waste must be carried out according to the appropriate policy. The correct bags must be used and they must be placed in the appropriate place. If this is not carried out the risk of infection is high and this must be minimised at all times.

Activity 6

Learners should be made aware of the importance of regularly checking the building to ensure it is safe and secure at all times. For example fire extinguishers must be maintained on a regular and systematic basis; alarms must function correctly; fire doors must remain closed and damaged or faulty equipment must be taken out of use.

1.2 Understand the role and responsibilities of the worker with regard to recognising potential and actual danger, harm and abuse

Care scenario, page 16

There is institutional abuse being carried out here and Stacey can play a part in addressing this. Stacey could speak to her manager or senior but must pass her concerns on.

Activity 7

A better version of the report might read:

21st October

Care report

Care worker Mim Price

Mac dressed himself with a little help. I also helped him to go to the toilet, and to wash and comb his hair.

Mac seemed tired and when I asked him he told me that he had not slept well again but was feeling well. I made a note to discuss this with his link worker as soon as possible to see if there is anything we can do to make the situation better.

I then asked Mac what he would like me to prepare for his lunch and he chose roast beef and salad.

The nurse then called after lunch to change his catheter. He cheered up in the afternoon and when I called back later I spent some time with him doing the exercises the physiotherapist had recommended. When I left he was listening to music on the radio.

1.3 Understand the role and responsibilities and boundaries of others with regard to safeguarding individuals from danger, harm and abuse

Activity 8

Each instance may be based around decisions made for a reason. For example, in statement 1, large amounts of funding may have been directed towards children's services in the preceding years. However, they may also be viewed as being discriminatory towards certain aspects or parts of the sector. Statement 2 does not make provision for other people who may not wish to eat meat; statement 3 is similar in approach. Adaptations are a vital part of living arrangements for people with disabilities.

Activity 9

Encourage learners to think about the situation from Mr Hughes' point of view. How is Mr Hughes feeling about all of this, and how he lives? It would seem that a complete care review would be needed here in order to establish responsibility for funding and the level of care required in order to care for Mr Hughes appropriately.

Activity 10

Managers require a broad range of skills and knowledge, including a good working knowledge of health and safety issues and requirements, a thorough knowledge of CSCI requirements, a good understanding of care planning and person-centred planning techniques, experience of managing staff and staff supervision, ability to communicate effectively both verbally and in writing, ability to prioritise and manage workload, ability to motivate staff and to build a rapport and maintain professional relationships with staff, individuals, their families as well as other professionals and agencies. This activity encourages trainers to gain knowledge of the diverse range of skills required by a manager and how this impacts on their role and the quality and level of service provided.

Activity 11

It is interesting to note the public perception of those working in social care, particularly social workers. What is their role and what part do they play in the protection of vulnerable individuals?

Are their actions always the right ones? For example, in the case of Victoria Climbié, the social worker was slated for not taking Victoria away from her carers.

Activity 12

This encourages debate around the role played by organisations, particularly the Police. It is often argued that the Police are too involved, or not involved enough. Do they have sufficient training to enable them to make decisions around incidents of abuse? Are their actions helpful or do they cause further issues?

Activity 13

This activity aims to facilitate some basic research into the support that is available. There are numerous regional, local and national groups that offer support in a variety of ways. There are support groups for all needs, for example, Mencap, Carer Support and Safeline UK.

1.4 Understand the sources of support for the worker following disclosure or discovery of abuse

Activity 14

Learners must be encouraged to think about teams and how they work. Teams must function effectively, and people are their most important ingredient. If a team is to function effectively, all the necessary skills and experience should be present and the people should have the authority to act on their own. Tuckman's stages of team development may be helpful here:

Forming – a formal stage and members treat each other as strangers.

Storming – members start to communicate their feelings but probably still view themselves as not yet part of the team.

Norming – people feel part of the team and realise that they can achieve things if they accept other viewpoints.

Performing – the team works in an open and trusting atmosphere where flexibility is the key and hierarchy is of little importance.

2.1 Understand the different types of abuse/harm

Activity 15

This is to encourage learners to become aware of the different signs and symptoms there may be. Recognising the signs is not always easy and it must be highlighted that observing signs or symptoms may not indicate that harm or abuse has been carried out, but it is still vital to report any concerns.

2.3 Understand the importance of recognising the indicators of abuse/harm

Activity 16

Learners are asked to write two possible signs or symptoms of abuse in each box. It is important that they are encouraged to think more broadly than the initial thoughts that may be based around cuts and bruises. Any changes to an individual's behaviour or appearance may be an indication that all is not well.

2.4 Understand the factors that can affect the individual, carer or social care worker that may lead to harm or abuse

Activity 17

The aim of this activity is to encourage learners to think about a time when they did not have enough sleep and the impact this can have on their ability to carry out tasks and make decisions. Ask them to imagine how it must feel to not have had a proper night's sleep for ages. This does not condone abuse being carried out, but does try to offer an insight into how a carer may feel and what leads to incidents.

2.5 Understand the effects of abuse on individuals

Activity 18

Learners are asked to consider the situation at the residential home. It may seem ideal for some, but is it? What can Alison do about this and what impact would this have on individuals? Often routine is helpful when working in this part of the sector, but too regimented a routine restricts choice and the promotion of independence. Discussion around approaches to best practice would highlight views on what is acceptable and what is not.

3.1 Understand the factors that affect the development of values and social norms, both for service users and for workers

Activity 19

What is normal? Learners will have views on what is acceptable and what is not. But even if they believe that something, for example the structure of a family, is not normal or acceptable, it may be that this works for those involved, therefore it is not for us to judge a situation based on our own values.

3.2 Understand how the points in 3.1 influence how situations may be perceived as abusive or protective

Activity 20

Learners should consider the issues around how Hassan is living. There are risks to his safety and well-being, but these must be weighed against the choices Hassan can make for himself.

Activity 21

Learners may not be fully aware of the vast range of skills and knowledge required to work in the sector, so this activity is to encourage ideas and suggestions around the most important qualities and skills required in order to deliver good quality care.

Activity 22

This activity explores the roles and responsibilities of individuals working in the sector and identifies very specific roles related to their job. Some roles will only be carried out by that individual, for example inspection, but other roles may be interchangeable, for example ensuring standards are met by the care setting is the responsibility of the manager and of all care staff.

3.3 Understand that regardless of perceptions an objective and professional response is required in situations of potential and actual danger, harm and abuse

Activity 23

When there is a risk of harm or abuse, who is responsible for minimising this, or for reporting any incidents? It is important that learners start to consider who plays these key roles in safeguarding and protecting individuals. The list may be long, and may include the Police, social services, CSCI, inspectors, care managers, carers and friends and relatives.

Activity 24

The key objective here is to raise awareness that abuse and harm can be carried out in many different ways. Using the wrong techniques is abuse and can cause harm, particularly if training has been carried out to demonstrate the correct way of doing things. This activity also introduces the importance of the role of inspection and how activities are viewed and reported.

4.1 Understand the legislation, regulations and guidance that govern the safeguarding of vulnerable adults from danger, harm and abuse

Activity 25

Learners are encouraged to think about aspects of their own work settings and how they can change them for the better. For example propping a fire door open may seem like a good idea but would in no way help in the event of a fire.

Care scenario, page 91

The DDA is a key element here and it has been breached as Mr Smyth did not attempt to communicate and actually put other people before Mrs Morgan.

Care scenario, page 92

This is to encourage learners to fully consider how the NSF can help people like Maria. Maria must be fully assessed and cared for.

Activity 26

Legislation underpins and supports the protection of vulnerable adults, therefore it is important that learners are made aware of the key legislation that is in place. Learners are not required to have a detailed knowledge of all the legislation, but should be aware of the key implications and requirements, particularly relating to their potential role in the sector.

Legislation relating to the protection of vulnerable adults – but which ones?				
Equal Opportunities Act	**The Misuse of Drugs Act (1971)**	**The Misuse of Drugs Regulations 2003**	**National Minimum Standards**	**The Data Protection Act 1998**
The Control of Substances Hazardous to Health	**EEC Directives**	**Local policies and procedures**	**The Care Standards Act 2000**	**The Human Rights Act 1998**
Road Traffic Act 1999	**Health and Safety at Work Act 1974**	The Income Tax (Trading and Other Income) Act 2005	Food Premises (Registration) Regulations 1991	The Transmissible Spongiform Encephalophathies (No. 2) Regulations 2006
Public Interest Disclosure Act (1998)	**Reporting of Injuries, Diseases and Dangerous Occurrences 1995**	**The Care Homes Regulations 2001**	**Children Act 2004**	**Protection of Vulnerable Adults Scheme (POVA)**

4.2 Understand the organisation's policies and procedures with regard to the safeguarding of vulnerable adults from danger, harm and abuse

Activity 27

This activity intends to highlight the use of complaints or compliments procedures. They are a requirement in the care sector but are used far more widely than learners may realise. What is also important about these procedures is that they are easily accessible, understood and implemented.

Student log

The following tables have been reproduced with the kind permission of Skills for Care. Use these tables to log your progress during your training and record the learning outcomes you have covered. The tables may also be used to map the content of an NVQ qualification or other relevant training course. For full details of how the knowledge set cross references to NVQ units, Common Induction Standards and GSCC Code of Practice (workers), please see the Skills for Care knowledge set document. Skills for Care documents can be found on the skillsforcare.org. website.

Main area	Learning outcome	Learning outcome achieved (manager's or trainer's signature)	Date
1. Roles and boundaries	**1.1** Understand the role, responsibilities and boundaries of the worker with regard to safeguarding individuals from danger, harm and abuse: ■ Person-centred approach (personal preferences and needs – cultural, social, religious) ■ Care planning ■ Risk assessment ■ 'No secrets' ■ Visitors to the setting (residential, domiciliary, day care) ■ Security of the setting ■ Environmental safety of the setting		
	1.2 Understand the role, responsibilities and boundaries of the worker with regard to recognising potential and actual danger, harm and abuse: ■ Observation ■ Monitoring ■ Reporting and recording		

Main area	Learning outcome	Learning outcome achieved (manager's or trainer's signature)	Date
	1.3 Understand the role and responsibilities and boundaries of others with regard to safeguarding individuals from danger, harm and abuse: ■ The individual ■ Family and friends ■ Independent advocate ■ Manager of service ■ Social worker ■ General practitioner ■ Police ■ Fire service ■ Specialist services ■ The Social Care Inspectorate		
	1.4 Understand the sources of support for the worker following disclosure or discovery of abuse: ■ Within the service setting (supervision, team support, counselling, training) ■ Outside the service setting (counselling services, Samaritans, General Practitioner, family and friends)		
2. Danger, harm and abuse	**2.1** Understand the different types of abuse/harm: ■ Physical ■ Neglect/acts of omission ■ Financial/material ■ Psychological ■ Sexual ■ Institutional ■ Discriminatory ■ Self harm/abuse ■ Racial		

Main area	Learning outcome	Learning outcome achieved (manager's or trainer's signature)	Date
	2.2 Understand that **anyone** may be *at risk* of abuse but especially those who are: ■ Lacking mental awareness ■ Lacking capacity ■ Severely physically disabled ■ Sensory impaired ■ Semi-comatose/comatose ■ Aphasic		
	2.3 Understand the importance of recognising the indicators of abuse/harm: ■ Physical (bruises, lacerations, abrasions, fractures, bites, burns, scalds, hair loss in one area, cowering, flinching) ■ Psychological (**changes** in any of: mood, behaviour, responsiveness, appetite, sleep patterns, continence, use of eye contact) ■ Neglect/acts of omission (e.g. lack of cleanliness – for the person and their environment, lack of aids to support daily life, malnutrition) ■ Financial/material (anxiety about money and payments, change in the ability to pay for goods and services, loss of personal possessions of value) ■ Institutional – in more than one person (unkempt and dirty, unusually subdued, lack of aids to support daily life, anxiety and fear in the presence of social care workers, drowsiness) ■ Self harm/abuse (bruises, lacerations, bites, scratches, hair loss in one area, unusual non-healing of sores, evidence of substance misuse) ■ Sexual (**changes** in mood and behaviour, attention seeking, withdrawal, uninhibited sexual behaviour and/or language, reluctance to undress, anxiety, evidence of infection or injury in the genital or rectal area)		

Main area	Learning outcome	Learning outcome achieved (manager's or trainer's signature)	Date
	2.4 Understand the factors which can affect the individual, carer or social care worker that may lead to harm or abuse: ■ Stress and anxiety ■ Illness ■ Sleep deprivation ■ Effects of substance misuse ■ Learned behaviours ■ Lack of support and guidance ■ Lack of training (social care worker) ■ Lack of employment and finances		
	2.5 Understand the effects of abuse on individuals: ■ Lack of confidence ■ Lack of self-esteem ■ Anxiety ■ Withdrawal ■ Depression ■ Subservient behaviour ■ Constant seeking of approval ■ Anger/aggression/abusive behaviour		
3. Social norms, values and perceptions	Note: **This part of the knowledge set introduces the opportunity for learners and learning providers to explore some of the dilemmas faced as a result of the variance in social norms and values. These may lead to difficult decisions for social care workers. There may be parallels with child protection and its impact on workers – see 'barriers' in the key words and concepts section of the Skills for Care document.** It is important to acknowledge that a situation may be regarded as abusive or protective depending on perspective, e.g. some individuals with autistic spectrum disorder may prefer or need a stark and uncluttered room even though the social norm would suggest that more comfortable and stimulating furnishings should be provided. The important point in all cases is that social care workers understand **why** a particular strategy or course of action has been adopted in order to provide the most appropriate care for an individual.		

Main area	Learning outcome	Learning outcome achieved (manager's or trainer's signature)	Date
	3.1 Understand the factors which affect the development of values and social norms, both for people who use services and for workers. These must be set in the context of safeguarding individuals from danger, harm and abuse. Factors include: ▪ Parenting styles (permissive, authoritative, authoritarian) ▪ Family dynamics (extended family, lone parenting, isolated family, same-gender family grouping) ▪ Class and cultural variations (status, wealth, beliefs) ▪ Education (formal, informal) ▪ Life experiences (history, illness, trauma, employment)		
	3.2 Understand how the points in 3.1 influence how situations may be perceived as abusive or protective by: ▪ The individual ▪ Family and friends ▪ Social care worker ▪ Manager of service ▪ Other professionals ▪ The care organisation ▪ The Social Care Inspectorate		
	3.3 Understand that regardless of perceptions an objective and professional response is required in situations of potential and actual danger, harm and abuse from: ▪ The social care worker ▪ Manager of the service ▪ The care organisation ▪ Other professionals ▪ The commissioning authority ▪ The Social Care Inspectorate		

Main area	Learning outcome	Learning outcome achieved (manager's or trainer's signature)	Date
4. Legislation and guidance in relation to the safe-guarding of vulnerable adults	**4.1** Understand the legislation, regulations and guidance that govern the safeguarding of vulnerable adults from danger, harm and abuse: ■ Health and Safety at Work Act 1974 ■ Management of Health and Safety at Work Act (amended 1994) ■ Human Rights Act 1998 ■ Care Standards Act 2000 ■ Safeguarding of Vulnerable Adults Scheme 2004 (based on Care Standards Act 2000) ■ 'No Secrets' – DH guidance ■ Health Act 1999 ■ Community Care Act 1990 ■ Mental Health Act 1983 ■ Mental Capacity Act 1983 amended 2005 ■ Data Protection Act 1998 ■ Disability Discrimination Act 1995 amended 2005 ■ National Service Framework for Older People ■ Race Relations Act 1976 and amendments 2000, 2003 ■ Enduring Power of Attorney Act 1985 ■ Freedom of Information Act 2000 ■ Sex Discrimination Act 1975 and amendments 1982, 1999 ■ Public Interest Disclosure Act 1998 ('whistle-blower's charter') ■ Modernising Social Services 1998 ■ Sexual Offences Act 2003 ■ Domestic Violence, Crime and Victims Act 2004		

Main area	Learning outcome	Learning outcome achieved (manager's or trainer's signature)	Date
	4.2 Understand the organisation's policies and procedures with regard to the safeguarding of vulnerable adults from danger, harm and abuse: ▪ Safe environment ▪ Secure environment ▪ Correct recruitment procedures for staff working in social care settings ▪ No secrets – including whistle-blowing ▪ Policy on visitors ▪ Complaints procedure		

Glossary

advocacy speaking up for another person to help them get their views across

advocate someone who can speak up to help another person's views be heard

authoritarian where the parents are in charge and children do as they are told

care planning a way of agreeing, arranging and managing the services or help needed to support someone to live at home, receive treatment or live in a more supported environment

competent properly or sufficiently qualified, capable or efficient

consent agreement or acceptance

Criminal Records Bureau (CRB) organisation that provides wider access to criminal record information through the disclosure service. This service enables organisations in the public, private and voluntary sectors to make safer recruitment decisions by identifying candidates who may be unsuitable for certain jobs, especially those that involve children or vulnerable adults. The CRB was established under Part V of the Police Act 1997 and was launched in March 2002

danger being at risk from harm or injury

discriminatory abuse unfair treatment of an individual, treating them less well than others, using any difference there may be as a reason

diversity individual characteristics or differences based on, for example, religion, culture, sexuality, gender or disability

dynamics how groups, families or individuals communicate, work, socialise or co-exist together

financial dependency relying on another person for money or resources

financial/material abuse the illegal use or misuse of property or items without permission from the person they belong to

gender reassignment altering primary characteristics of sex and roles

institutional abuse neglect or a routine that offers little or no choice

inter-agency framework organisations demonstrating how they intend to plan and work together towards shared goals

local authority regional council or local government

multi-disciplinary team team whose members work together to deliver services

neglect/acts of omission failure to provide care, food, warmth, clothes or treatment

'No Secrets' guidance on developing and implementing multi-agency policies and procedures to protect vulnerable adults from abuse

observation looking at the actions and well-being of an individual

over-medication giving an individual additional medication to keep them quiet or calm so that they will be less trouble

person-centred approach assessing an individual's needs, putting them at the centre of the process

physical abuse inflicting pain or injury on an individual

prejudice judging someone or having an idea about them without actually knowing anything about them

Protection of Vulnerable Adults (POVA) a scheme launched by the Department of Health in 2004. At the heart of the POVA scheme is the POVA list of care workers who have harmed vulnerable adults in their care. From 26 July 2004, registered care providers must request a check against the POVA list when considering a person for a care position

psychological abuse upsetting or humiliating an individual using words or actions

rights legal or moral entitlement to choice, freedom, privacy and services

self-esteem an individual's confidence in themselves

sexual abuse any sexual act that is carried out without permission

stereotypes generalisations or assumptions that people make about the characteristics of all members of a group, based on an (often wrong) image about what people in that group are like

stress emotional and physical strain caused by how we respond to different pressures

tactile to do with the sense of touch, communicating using touch

Index

Illustrations are indicated by **bold** page numbers.